PRACTICING WRITING PROCESS

WRITING IN THE CONTENT AREAS

BY
SHEILA C. CROWELL
&
ELLEN D. KOLBA

EDUCATIONAL DESIGN, INC.   EDI 273

ACKNOWLEDGMENTS

The following selections are reprinted with the kind permission of the publishers:

AUGUST HEAT, from *The Beast with Five Fingers: Twenty Tales of the Uncanny* by William Fryer Harvey. Copyright 1947 by E.P. Dutton. Reprinted by permission of the publisher, E.P. Dutton, a division of NAL Penguin Inc.

THE MAN HE KILLED, from *The Complete Poems of Thomas Hardy*, edited by James Gibson (New York: Macmillan, 1978)

THE SNIPER, from *Spring Sowing* by Liam O'Flaherty. Reprinted by permission of Harcourt Brace Jovanovich, Inc.

A MOTHER IN MANNVILLE, from *When the Whippoorwill*, by Marjorie Kinnan Rawlings. Copyright 1940 Marjorie Kinnan Rawlings; copyright renewed © 1968 Norton Baskin. Reprinted with the permission of Charles Scribner's Sons.

THE VIRGINIA COLONY and **THE MASSACHUSETTS COLONIES** by Hilarie Staton, excerpts from a work in progress to be published by Educational Design, Inc. Copyright pending.

All other text and resource selections written by the authors.

The authors would like to thank the teachers and students in the following school districts who provided samples of student writing and gave us invaluable feedback on the ideas and activities in this book:

The Chicago, IL, Public Schools
The Montclair, NJ, Public Schools
The Paterson, NJ, Public Schools
Beaumont, TX, Independent School District
Corpus Christi, TX, ISD
Deer Park, TX, ISD
Dickinson, TX, ISD
Irving, TX, ISD
North Forest, TX, ISD

ISBN# 0-87694-063-7   EDI 273

Table of Contents

940166

Introduction

When you write essays in school about topics in literature or history or science, you are writing in different content areas. Yet although the subject matter of the content areas may differ, the types of thinking and organizing you have to do when you write your essays are very similar. Comparing and contrasting two characters in a play, for example, is not very different from comparing and contrasting two historical figures or events.

This book is about how to write essays in different content areas. It has several purposes:

- To help you think more clearly and to organize your thoughts more effectively.

- To give you practice in answering the kinds of questions that are often asked in classes in different content areas—classes in literature, history, science, home economics, career education, and so on.

- To give you practice in different kinds of writing: definitions, summaries, expository paragraphs, editorials, process papers, and position papers.

- To help you write better essays and compositions by using the steps of the writing process—prewriting, writing, and revising.

Because thinking is the most important part of writing, each of the five units in this book deals with some aspect of thinking:

- Defining

- Comparing and Contrasting

- Organizing and Analyzing

- Expressing Opinions

- Making Judgments

In each unit, the first lesson introduces the kind of thinking emphasized in the writing tasks that follow. You may not do much actual writing in this first lesson, but you will work with ideas and techniques that are essential to the writing that you will do in the rest of the unit.

The lessons that follow consist of two parts. The first part of the lesson gives you a chance to work on sections of a full-length essay by completing the prewriting, writing, and revising of a sample composition. The second part of the lesson consists of a checklist that will help you produce an essay of the same kind. In addition, the last lesson in each unit gives you a topic on which to write an essay of your own.

You cannot write essays in different content areas without some content, of course. At the end of the book are several resource selections for you to read at different times as you go through this book. Shorter resource selections are contained within the lessons themselves.

UNIT ONE: DEFINING AND DESCRIBING

One of the simplest kinds of writing you are asked to do is to give a short definition or description of something you have read about in a textbook.

One of the most subtle kinds of writing you may be asked to do is the character sketch—a paragraph or short essay that vividly and accurately describes a person in history or in a work of literature.

Both kinds of descriptive writing require you to use the thinking skill of spotting what is characteristic and unique about something or somebody—what identifies them among all the other things or people that they may resemble.

This unit will show you how to handle a variety of descriptive writing tasks and assignments. You will be reading and writing in the following content areas:

- Science
- Literature

1. Writing Definitions

Every subject you study in school has special words that you may be asked to define for home-work assignments or as part of an exam. The exercises in this lesson will show you what a good definition consists of and will give you practice in writing good definitions of your own. Just as important, you will learn to sharpen your thinking skills so that whatever you write will be more precise as well as more complete.

The Parts of a Definition

Which of these is a good definition?

> A chair is a piece of furniture.
>
> A chair is for one person to sit on.
>
> A chair has four legs, a back, and a seat.

Each of these sentences tells you something about a chair. But each one is incomplete.

> A chair is a piece of furniture BUT—so is a bed.
>
> A chair is for one person to sit on BUT—so is a stool.
>
> A chair has four legs, a back, and a seat BUT—so does a couch.

A good definition of a chair would combine all three statements:

> A chair is a piece of furniture for one person to sit on that has four legs, a back, and a seat.

Every good definition begins the same way: **by naming the thing to be defined**:

> NAME
> A chair

Then a **category** it belongs to is mentioned:

> NAME   CATEGORY
> A chair   is   a piece of furniture

The final part of the definition consists of one or two **important details that identify it** and make it special:

> NAME   CATEGORY   IDENTIFYING DETAILS
> A chair   is   a piece of furniture 1. for one person to sit on
>   2. that has four legs, a back, and a seat

Anyone who reads this definition now knows what category a chair belongs to and something about its purpose and design.

Practice 1

Try defining these words. Write the word you are defining. Then say what category it belongs to. Finally, write one or two identifying details that are special about it, such as its purpose or its design.

1. table

_____

_____

2. desk

_____

_____

3. bed

_____

_____

4. couch

_____

_____

5. dresser

_____

_____

Choosing Categories

The first step in defining something, after writing the word you are defining, is to name the category it belongs to.

Practice 2

Write the name of the category to which each of the following groups of items belongs. The first one has been done for you as an example.

ITEMS	CATEGORY
1. bass, keyboard, drum	Musical Instruments
2. boots, slippers, sneakers	_____
3. English, French, Spanish	_____

continued...

4. biology, chemistry, physics   _____

5. horse, cow, goat   _____

6. sleet, snow, rain   _____

7. Denmark, Sweden, Norway   _____

8. silk, wool, cotton   _____

9. Army, Navy, Marine Corps   _____

10. red, blue, yellow   _____

Practice 3

A. Now try an exercise that practices the opposite skill. Each item in the following exercise consists of a category and one specific example. Add two other specific examples of your own.

1. Headgear
    cowboy hat   _____   _____

2. Predators
    lion   _____   _____

3. Electronic Devices
    digital watch   _____   _____

4. World Problems
    famine   _____   _____

5. Part-time Jobs
    babysitting   _____   _____

6. Rights Guaranteed to
   Americans
    freedom of
    speech   _____   _____

7. Difficult Sports
    rock climbing   _____   _____

8. Boring Chores
    cleaning room   _____   _____

continued...

B. From the exercise above, pick 4 of the examples you wrote and start a series of definitions. You will complete these definitions later. EXAMPLE: A tiger (if that's one of your examples) is a predator....

1. _____

2. _____

3. _____

4. _____

Practice 4

For each of the following numbered items, choose the word or phrase that best identifies what category it belongs to. (Remember, a category is a *general* kind of thing, not a specific detail.) Put a check mark before the letter of your choice. The first one has been done for you.

1. winter

   a. when nights are long and days are short
   b. cold
   ✓ **c.** season

2. computer

   a. that solves problems
   b. machine
   c. controlled by a program

3. parent

   a. who worries about you all your life
   b. who brings you up
   c. person

4. giraffe

   a. with spots
   b. animal
   c. that runs away from leopards

5. basketball

   a. where each side scores points
   b. throwing a ball through a hoop high above the floor
   c. team sport

Practice 5

Write a definition for each of the the numbered words in Practice 4. Use the characteristics listed below each word in Practice 4 in constructing your definition. The first one has been done for you.

1. Winter is the season when it is cold and when nights are long and days are short. (Notice that the first characteristic in your definition is the category of things to which the word belongs.)

2. A computer is a _____.

   _____

3. A parent is a _____.

   _____

4. A giraffe is a _____.

   _____

5. Basketball is a _____.

   _____

Practice 6

Construct your own definition exercise by choosing five items from the list below and following the pattern of Practice Exercises 4 and 5.

pizza	friend	dishwasher
spring	chess	cartoonist
sneakers	algebra	hockey
leopard		

Adding Details

After you have decided what category an item belongs to, you will need to state what makes it different from all other items in the category. A table is a piece of furniture, but so is a chair. A Great Dane is a dog, but so is a cocker spaniel. To make your definitions more precise, you will need to add the kinds of specific, identifying details that tell what makes the thing you are defining different from other items in the same category. Here are three sets of definitions that illustrate some of the kinds of identifying details you might consider.

1. A Great Dane is a dog.
   A dachshund is a dog.

   But each has a different SIZE AND SHAPE.

A Great Dane is one of the largest of the dog breeds. It has smooth fur, long legs, and is very muscular.

A dachshund is one of the smallest of the dog breeds. It has smooth brown fur, a very long body, and short legs.

2. A station wagon is an automobile.
   A sports car is an automobile.

But each has a different FUNCTION.

A station wagon is an automobile designed to carry large objects and lots of people around the neighborhood and on long trips.

A sports car is an automobile designed for speed and looks. It usually carries only one or two people.

3. Figure skating is an ice sport.
   Hockey is an ice sport.

But each has a different PURPOSE.

Figure skating is an ice sport in which one person demonstrates agility and grace in a series of complex, dancelike movements.

Hockey is an ice sport played by opposing teams in which the object is to score goals by moving a black disk called a puck across the ice and through the opposing team's goal line.

Practice 7

Each of the following sets of definitions are identical—and incomplete. Make them different—and more complete—by adding specific details. Start by copying each definition and then add the details.

1. A cat is a furry house pet.
   A dog is a furry house pet.
   [HINT: Add details about their different functions.]

   A cat_____

   _____

   A dog_____

   _____

continued...

2. Checkers is a board game played on different-colored squares.
Chess is a board game played on different-colored squares.
[HINT: Add a sentence to each definition that tells about the object of the game.]

_____

_____

_____

_____

3. A donkey is a gray plant-eating animal.
A mouse is a gray plant-eating animal.
An elephant is a gray plant-eating animal.
[HINT: Add details about size and shape of each animal. Or mention such things as tusks, trunk, feet. You could also tell where each is commonly found.]

_____

_____

_____

_____

_____

_____

4. Football is a ball game.
Baseball is a ball game.
[HINT: Add details about number of players, size/shape of field, size of ball, how points are scored. You may need to use two sentences for each.]

_____

_____

_____

_____

_____

5. Geometry is a mathematical subject.
Algebra is a mathematical subject.
[HINT: begin the rest of each definition with the words "that deals with."]

_____

_____

_____

_____

Practice 8

Go back to Practice 3B. On the lines below, write the complete definition of each of the words you began to define in that exercise. When you write, think about what makes each thing special in its category. Ask yourself—

- Is it a different size or shaped differently?

- Does it do different things?

- Does it have a different purpose?

1. _____

   _____

2. _____

   _____

3. _____

   _____

4. _____

   _____

2. Writing Short-Answer Homework Assignments

Content Area: Science

Many homework assignments and final exams ask you to answer questions in one or two sentences. You may be asked to "define" or "describe" or "identify" an event, a process, or a theory in science, social studies or history, home economics, or health. Whatever the subject, the procedure is the same. This lesson will help you learn to use your textbook to find the answers to these questions quickly. It will also show you how to write the best kind of short-answer assignments.

Finding Definitions in Textbooks

Many textbooks ask for short-answer definitions at the end of a chapter. If the word or term you have to define is important enough to become an end-of-chapter question, you can be sure that it is somewhere in plain sight in the chapter itself. Often it is written in **boldface**—dark type **like this.**

EXAMPLE 1

The Respiratory System

Oxygen is important to all animal life. Without it, fish could not swim, birds could not fly, and humans could not walk or run or think. All animals have some method of taking oxygen from the environment and returning carbon dioxide to the environment. This process of exchange is known as **respiration**. . .

Sometimes definitions are put in a footnote at the bottom of a page, as in the following example:

EXAMPLE 2

How the Human Respiratory System Works

Let us look at how the human respiratory system works. When we breathe, we contract the **diaphragm**[1], which increases the size of the chest cavity, which in turn causes the air pressure in the lungs to drop. In response to that drop in pressure, air moves in from the outside. We take in this air through the nose, where it is warmed up before moving farther into the body. The nose also filters dust out of the air. . .

---

[1]diaphragm—a muscle in the chest that allows breathing to take place

Other places for definitions are in a boxed glossary at the beginning of a chapter or in a glossary at the back of the book. Occassionally important terms are defined in the index. Editors and writers want you to know these terms, so they make them easy to find.

Sometimes your teacher will supply you with a sheet of definitions. SAVE THEM. MEMORIZE THEM. USE THEM.

Practice 1

Use what you have learned about finding definitions in textbooks to answer the following questions. Read the question, read the example you have chosen, and write the answer in the blank.

1. Which of the examples on the previous page contains a definition of respiration? _____

2. Which of the following best describes the category to which respiration belongs?

   a. event
   b. theory
   c. process

3. Define respiration.

   _____

   _____

   _____

4. Evaluate your definition.

   ● Did I name the category?_____

   ● Did I mention that respiration is something animals do? _____

   ● Did I write a complete sentence?_____

   If you did not answer yes to all three questions, examine your definition and make the necessary changes.

5. Write the definition of **diaphragm.** _____

   _____

6. Where does this definition appear? _____

7. Which example explains the function of the nose in human respiration?

   _____

8. Does the example state the category to which the nose belongs?

   _____

9. To which of these categories does the nose most clearly belong?

   a. process
   b. muscle
   c. body part

10. Define the word **nose,** identifying the category to which it belongs and completing the definition with two functions that the nose performs in respiration.

    _____

    _____

    _____

Adding the Right Details

When you are asked to describe something in a few sentences, the additional information you give must be very important. It must be almost as important as the definition itself.

For example, look at this definition of a camera:

A camera is a device for taking photographs.

Which of the following would be good to add to make a longer definition? Put a check mark before the additional information that makes a more complete definition.

a. It contains a box to hold the film and a lens that lets the light come through.

b. My dad's camera was made in Japan.

c. It takes a lot of practice to take good pictures.

d. Taking vacation photos is a popular hobby for American families.

If you checked *a,* you were correct. Adding essential physical characteristics is a good way to extend a definition.

Choice *b* is personal information. It does not belong in a definition.

Choice *c* does not add essential information. The sentence would be perfectly acceptable, however, in a paragraph about picture-taking.

The final choice, *d,* is also nonessential information. It belongs in a paragraph about what cameras are used for.

Practice 2

In this exercise you get a chance to practice answering the kinds of questions asked in homework assignments or in exams. Note the form of the question. The first part of the answer is given to you. Your job is to complete each definition by choosing the most essential piece of information from each group of facts. Write the completed definition on the lines given. You may use two sentences for your definition, or you may combine the elements.

1. *What is boiling?*

Boiling is a cooking technique in which foods are placed in heated water.
a. It makes foods mushy if they are boiled too long.
b. Microwaving has replaced boiling in many American homes.
c. The water is heated to 212°F and maintained at that temperature for the time required.
d. Many small children are injured when boiling water is spilled on them.

_____

_____

_____

continued...

2. *Identify George Washington.*

George Washington was the first American President.

  a. He was offered the opportunity to be king of America and turned it down.

  b. He was the victorious commander-in-chief of the Continental Army and was the unanimous choice of Congress for President.

  c. He had fought on the side of the English in the French and Indian War.

  d. In his youth he had been a surveyor and had learned a lot about the land and its people.

_____

_____

_____

3. *What is a novel?*

A novel is a book-length work of fiction.

  a. Many novels are published every year.

  b. Most people read novels in paperback.

  c. Some of the best novelists are women.

  d. It usually contains a complex plot and a variety of characters.

_____

_____

_____

4. *Define soccer.*

Soccer is a ball game.

  a. A soccer ball is smaller than a basketball.

  b. In Great Britain, soccer is simply called "football."

  c. In soccer the ball can be moved only by the feet.

  d. Americans are now playing more soccer than ever before.

_____

_____

_____

continued...

5. *Define continental drift.*

Continental drift is a theory about how the surface of the Earth moves.
  a. Scientists noticed that on the map the shape of Africa seemed to fit the shape of South America.
  b. Each section of the Earth's surface can be thought of as resting on a movable plate that gradually drifts across the globe.
  c. It causes volcanos and builds mountains.
  d. At first it didn't seem possible.

_____

_____

_____

The Language of Definitions

Notice that in all the definitions you have been working with so far, the pattern is the same. The definition always begins with the word or term that is being defined.

What is the TRW cycle?

Acceptable: The TRW cycle is the process by which...

Unacceptable: The process by which...

Repeating the words does two things. It helps the person who is correcting your papers find your answer quickly. More important, it helps YOU. When you learn the whole definition, you have a better chance of remembering it. (Why? The human mind just works that way.) Always repeat the word or phrase when you are asked to define something in this book.

Practice 3

Read the following excerpt from an earth science book. It describes a structure that helps fish float. Then answer the questions.

The Air Bladder: A Pressure Organ.
A thin-walled sac, the air bladder, lies in the upper part of the body cavity of the fish. Most fish get oxygen from the water that passes over their gills. The oxygen then travels through the body and helps inflate the bladder. Nitrogen and carbon dioxide are other gases that inflate the bladder along with the oxygen.

The bladder acts as a float. It allows the fish to remain at any water depth without much effort. By adjusting the amount of gas in the air bladder, the fish can move to different levels in the water. The air bladder expands or contracts as the fish goes higher or lower in the water. When a fish that is adjusted to a great depth is caught

continued...

and quickly brought to surface, the air bladder expands. This can push the fish's stomach up into its mouth. Some fish, like the mackerel and the shark, have no air bladder. These fish must keep swimming in order to remain afloat. As soon as they stop swimming, they sink to the bottom.

1. What category of things does an air bladder belong to? (Write a short, complete sentence, beginning "An air bladder is...")

   _____

2. Write another sentence that gives a physical description of the air bladder, including its location.

   _____

   _____

3. Write a third sentence, identifying the function of an air bladder.

   _____

4. Add an interesting fact that you learned from the excerpt.

   _____

5. Put all these sentences together. You may combine sentences wherever it makes the definition read more smoothly.

   _____

   _____

   _____

   _____

   _____

   _____

   _____

3. Describing a Character

Content Area: Literature
Resource Selection: "How Anansi Stole All the Wisdom in the World,"
page 134

One of the commonest writing assignments in literature is the character sketch. The writer must read the selection, think about the things that make a character special, try to sum up the character in a sentence or two, and then write a paragraph or short essay that makes the character seem so real you think you could recognize him or her. Like a good definition, a character sketch is precise and complete. This lesson will apply the thinking and writing skills you used in the first two lessons. You will help a student complete a character sketch. Then you will write one on your own.

Sam's Character Sketch

Sam's class read the story "How Anansi Stole All the Wisdom in the World," which begins on page 134 of this book. Turn to page 134 and read the story before you go any further in this chapter.

―――――――――――――――――――――― ❑ ――――――――――――――――――――――

After reading and discussing the story, Sam's class was given the following assignment:

Write a one-paragraph character sketch of Kweku. Tell what you think he is like by using details from the story. Describe the qualities that make him special. End your paragraph with one sentence that sums up what kind of person he is.

What is *your* first impression of Kweku? Write a few words to describe him. They do not have to be in sentences.

―――

―――

Prewriting

Sam wrote a list of questions to help him find out more about the character of Kweku. Then he wrote one or two words as partial answers.

Here are Sam's questions and answers. Read them carefully. Notice that from time to time you will be asked to add something to what Sam wrote.

Complete Sam's answers for him.

How does Kweku act towards other people? Kind, gentle

How does he feel about his work? Takes pride, _____

How does he feel about his father? Amused by him, _____

What do his actions tell you about what he is like as a person?

Peaceful, _____

Next, Sam made two columns. The first column was for qualities he had found. In the second column he gave examples or incidents from the story.

Complete the chart with incidents from the story.

QUALITIES	EXAMPLES AND INCIDENTS
kind, gentle	doesn't get mad at the monkey
pride, care	happy that others know he is good
amused by him, loves him	smiles at father's tricks accepts his father with all his faults
peaceful	doesn't get upset when father empties water barrel
intelligent	uses his brain to handle monkey

Now Sam had enough details to begin writing his first draft.

Writing

Here is what Sam wrote. Notice how he used the details from the list he made.

Kweku is a very gentle person who doesn't get upset at many things. When a very active monkey comes into his workplace to make a mess and try to steal things, Kweku doesn't raise his voice or use a stick. He is smart enough to use his brain, and tricks the monkey. Kweku is an artist, and he takes pride in his work. His father, Anansi Spider, is the sort of person who could drive anyone crazy, but Kweku just acts amused whenever Anansi does outrageous things. Even when the Spider Man poured all of Kweku's water on the ground, Kweku just shrugged it off. He also has a lot of common sense.

Revising

After Sam wrote the draft, he knew he wanted to add some things.

What do you think he needs to add?

_____

_____

Sam knew that he needed to add examples to support two of the statements he made in the paragraph.

Write the supporting sentences that Sam omitted.

Kweku is an artist and takes pride in his work. _____

_____

_____

He also has a lot of common sense. _____

_____

_____

Sam also needed to make a general statement at the end that would sum up some special quality that Kweku possessed. He read over the list of details, looking for what they had in common, and added the following to his notes:

special quality -- respect for everything (name some things he has respect for -- including Anansi)

Sam added this sentence at the end of the paragraph.

Complete the sentence for him.

What makes Kweku so special is the respect he has . . . _____

_____

_____

_____

_____

Editing

As a final step, Sam proofread his letter and corrected errors he had made in grammar, usage, spelling, and punctuation. Then he made a fresh copy to hand in.

Your Character Sketch

Write a character sketch of Anansi. Follow the steps that Sam did.

You can use the following checklist to help plan your essay and to evaluate it when you have finished.

☐ **1.** List details from the story that give clues to Anansi's character. Group the details under these headings:

- What Anansi thinks about himself
- What he thinks about other animals or people
- How he deals with problems

☐ **2.** Try to sum up Anansi's character in a one-sentence definition. Use these words as part of your definition:

  Anansi is the kind of person who...

☐ **3.** Write a draft of your sketch. Don't worry about getting everything right the first time. Just put all your thoughts down in a way that makes sense to you.

☐ **4.** Reread your sketch and decide what you want to add or change. Make sure that you have included your one-sentence definition. Also be sure that you back up your statements with details from the story.

☐ **5.** Edit and proofread your letter to correct errors in grammar, usage, spelling, and punctuation. Make a fresh copy.

UNIT TWO: COMPARING AND CONTRASTING

Every young child knows that elephants and rhinoceroses are both huge, gray, hairless animals that have thick skins and legs like tree trunks and that live in far-off places like India and Africa. But every child also knows that the two animals are very different. A rhino has short legs and one or two horns on its nose. An elephant has long legs, tusks, and a trunk.

We have been comparing and contrasting many things, not just rhinos and elephants, from our earliest childhood. This unit will show you how to handle comparisons and contrasts in your writing. You will be reading and writing in the following content areas:

- Consumer Education/Home Economics

- Literature

- Social Studies/American History

1. Identifying Similarities and Differences

When you describe the way two things are similar or alike, you are **comparing** *them. When you describe the differences between them, you are* **contrasting** *them. Writing assignments in school frequently ask you to compare and contrast—two characters in a story, two events in history, two ways of making something in shop or in home economics. This lesson will help you with the thinking skills you will use when you write about similarities and differences.*

Look at the two shapes below. Ask yourself: In what ways are they alike? In what ways are they different?

You can easily compare and contrast simple shapes like these. But not everything can be compared or contrasted. If things are either too much alike or too different, you won't learn anything from a comparison or contrast.

For example, look at these pictures:

Think about these questions:

Would there be any point in comparing the two squares? Why or why not?

Would there be any point in contrasting one of the squares and the eagle? Why or why not?

Which two pictures would it make sense to compare? Why?

Which two would it make sense to contrast? Why?

Practice 1

In the list below, put a check mark next to each pair of things that it would make sense to compare or contrast. Leave blank anything that it would <u>not</u> make sense to compare or contrast.

Examples:

   ✔a bird / an airplane
    a motorcycle / a brick house

---

continued...

1. a washing machine / a television set

2. the sun / the moon

3. a magazine / a rug

4. a cat / a comb

5. a doll / a baby

6. a house / a lake

7. a question / an answer

8. a game / a battle

9. a galaxy / a bus stop

10. a work day / a vacation day

Practice 2

Before you can compare or contrast things, you must know what they are like. One way to find out what things are like is to **characterize** or **define** them, the way you did in Unit One. For each object below, list six qualities or characteristics that describe it. Complete the list for the first object before you start the second one. Don't compare or contrast the two objects now. Just write words that describe or define each one.

Examples:

ORANGE	LEMON
tough skin	sour
sweet	has seeds
orange	scent used in detergent and furniture
grows on trees	polish
juice used as breakfast drink	tough skin
round	yellow
	used as flavoring

1. CASTLE   OFFICE BUILDING

_____   _____

_____   _____

_____   _____

_____   _____

_____   _____

_____   _____

continued...

2. HAND

FOOT

_____   _____
_____   _____
_____   _____
_____   _____
_____   _____
_____   _____

3. LAKE

OCEAN

_____   _____
_____   _____
_____   _____
_____   _____
_____   _____

4. THE UNITED STATES

JAPAN

_____   _____
_____   _____
_____   _____
_____   _____
_____   _____

Practice 3

Look back at the two lists you made for each pair above. How many of the qualities or characteristics you named are the same for both things? Go back to each pair of lists. Draw a solid line to connect the items in each pair that are the same. Draw a dotted line to connect any that contrast with each other or name differences. Follow the example on the next page—and notice that some items will not be connected.

Examples:

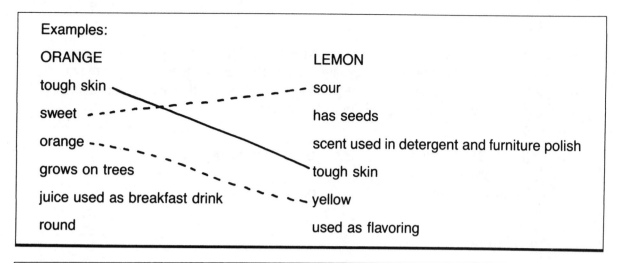

ORANGE   LEMON

tough skin   sour

sweet   has seeds

orange   scent used in detergent and furniture polish

grows on trees   tough skin

juice used as breakfast drink   yellow

round   used as flavoring

Practice 4

Look again at your lists in Practice 2, above. In particular, look at every characteristic that is *not* connected by a line to something in the opposite column. For every "unconnected" item, do one of the following three things:

—If the characteristic could go in the opposite column as well, write it there. Connect the two identical characteristics by a solid line.

—If a contrasting or opposite characteristic could go in the opposite column, write it there. Connect the two contrasting characteristics by a dotted line.

—If the characteristic is a unique quality, without any matching or contrasting characteristic that could go in the other column, put an asterisk (*) in front of it.

Examples:

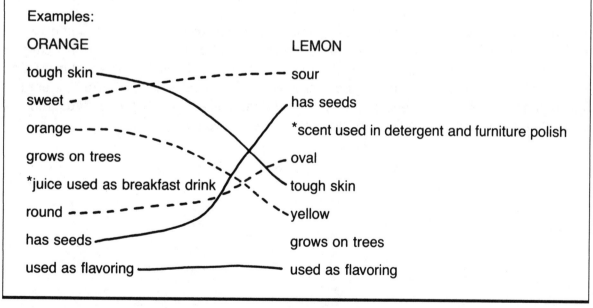

ORANGE   LEMON

tough skin   sour

sweet   has seeds

orange   *scent used in detergent and furniture polish

grows on trees   oval

*juice used as breakfast drink   tough skin

round   yellow

has seeds   grows on trees

used as flavoring   used as flavoring

When you list characteristics or qualities, you are listing details. This is the first step in comparing or contrasting two things. Words like "orange" and "sour" and "round" describe something specific. You need to go beyond these specifics, though, and discover the general terms that name these likenesses or differences. Then you will be able to do more than list characteristics when you write about comparisons and contrasts.

Practice 5

Each pair of words below consists of opposites or contrasting items, but both words are specific examples of some general quality or characteristic. Write the name of the quality or characteristic in the blank. (It might help to look back at the first lesson in this book on definitions and to review how to write a definition.)

Example:

CONTRASTING WORDS	GENERAL QUALITY
orange/yellow	color
stubborn/cooperative	behavior

1. sweet/sour _____

2. crisp/soft _____

3. huge/tiny _____

4. gentle/forceful _____

5. round/oblong _____

6. one inch/one yard _____

7. newborn/ancient _____

8. happy/miserable _____

9. ounce/ton _____

10. dim/glaring _____

When you have to write a paragraph about similarities or differences, it helps to start off with a list of characteristics and qualities like the ones you have been working with in this chapter. Here, for example, are two short paragraphs about oranges and lemons. The first is a COM-PARE paragraph, which concentrates on similarities. The second is a CONTRAST paragraph, which concentrates on differences. As you read them, notice what each one takes from the example list in Practice 4. Notice also what each one leaves out.

I: COMPARE

Although they taste quite different, an orange and a lemon have many things in common. First of all, they are citrus fruits that grow on trees. Their skins are different colors, but they are both tough, and they both encase a pulpy, seed-filled interior. Both the orange and the lemon can be squeezed to produce a drink that is popular on hot summer days, although we usually add water and sugar to lemon juice to make lemonade. And both are used to flavor candies, popsicles, and cakes.

II: CONTRAST

Because they are both tough-skinned citrus fruits, oranges and lemons may seem alike. A closer look, or better yet, a taste, shows how different they are. The round orange is sweet-tasting, while the oval lemon is sour. We eat oranges as fruit, but not lemons. The orange is squeezed to make a breakfast drink. The lemon finds its way into detergent and furniture polish. Not only do they differ in shape, flavor, and use, their color sets them apart. The orange is fiery inside and out, while the lemon pales in comparison.

Notice the following things about these two paragraphs:

- The Compare paragraph actually begins with a contrast ("they taste quite different"), and the Contrast paragraph begins with a comparison ("they are both tough-skinned citrus fruits"). This is a good way to make the start of your paragraph interesting. It's boring to start off with something like "Here is how oranges and lemons are similar," or "Oranges and lemons are quite different from each other."

- The paragraphs contain different kinds of sentences. It's dull to write like this: "Oranges are sweet but lemons are sour. Oranges are round but lemons are oval."

Practice 6

Turn one final time to Practice 2. Select one pair from that activity to write about. Look at the characteristics you identified as alike and the ones you identified as different. What general statements can you make about them? Use these as the basis of two short paragraphs, modeled on the examples above. In one paragraph, compare the two items. In the other paragraph, contrast them. Add whatever specific details and generalizations you need. Use the sentences given below to help you get started.

I: COMPARISON

Although they _____ different, a

_____ and a _____

are alike in some ways. First of all, _____

_____

_____

_____

_____

_____

_____

II: CONTRAST

Although they are both _____,

a _____ and a _____

are different in many ways. First of all, _____

_____

_____

_____

_____

_____

_____

2. *Weighing Advantages and Disadvantages*

Content Areas: *Consumer Education, Home Economics*
Resource Selection: *"How to Become a Smart Shopper," page 136*

Exploring the advantages and disadvantages of something is one of the simplest forms of comparing and contrasting. When you write about advantages and disadvantages, you are often dealing with only one topic, and it is easy to organize your writing. You will see how in this lesson, which deals with an everyday subject in the field of consumerism.

Gus's Paragraphs

Gus's class in consumer education has just finished reading a chapter on how to become a smart shopper and how to make your money go farther. Each student was asked to write one or two paragraphs telling about the advantages and disadvantages of some shopping practice, such as shopping for special sales or shopping in stores near where you live. The students were to use the information in the text as background and to add details from their own experience. Gus decided to write about the advantages and disadvantages of using fresh foods.

Before you go further in this chapter, read the excerpt on " How to Become a Smart Shopper" from Gus's textbook. As you read, notice the arguments both for and against each point raised. The selection begins on page 136.

—————————————— ❑ ——————————————

Now that you have read the selection, can you think of one additional advantage or disadvantage that you could add from your own experience? If so, write it here:

———————————————————————————————————————

———————————————————————————————————————

Prewriting

Gus knew something about his topic from doing the family shopping and from cooking meals for his brother and sister when his parents were working late. He also had a part-time job in a restaurant and was beginning to learn about food buying and preparation there.

Gus went through the material in the textbook again, looking for both advantages and disadvantages. (Notice that he found information not just under the heading "Deciding What to Buy" but also under the heading "A Guide to Stores.") He made two columns—one headed "Advantages" and the other headed "Disadvantages." Here is what Gus wrote in the first column:

ADVANTAGES

taste better

more nutritious

less harmful (no additives)

low prices sometimes (esp. at roadside stands)

Write the "Disadvantages" column for him. Use the resource material to guide you.

DISADVANTAGES

_____

_____

_____

_____

Gus checked his lists to make sure that he had enough details for at least one paragraph. He also wanted to be sure that he had about the same number of details under each head. That way his paragraph would be balanced—equally divided between advantages and disadvantages. If he wrote two paragraphs, one could deal with the advantages and the other with the disadvantages, and his paragraphs would still be balanced.

Is Gus's list of details balanced? If not, add or take out some details to make it more balanced. If you wish, add the advantage or disadvantage that you wrote down at the beginning of this lesson.

Writing

Gus ended up writing two paragraphs.

Use the details in Gus's two lists to complete these two paragraphs.

An advantage of fresh foods, especially fruits and vegetables, is that they taste much better than canned or frozen foods. _____

_____

_____

_____

Fresh foods have some disadvantages, too. It takes time to clean them and cook them, and there's more cleaning up to do afterwards. __

_____

_____

_____

Revising

Gus reread his paper. This is what it looked like. How close is it to the version you wrote?

An advantage of fresh foods, especially fruits and vegetables, is that they taste much better than canned or frozen foods. They are also better for you. They have more vitamins in them, and they have no preservatives or additives. You can also save money buying them. Farmers often sell fresh fruits and vegetables at roadside stands for lower prices than you can find in the supermarket.

Fresh foods have some disadvantages, too. It takes time to clean them and cook them, and there's more cleaning up to do afterwards. Fresh foods spoil easily. If you don't use them right away or if you buy more than you need, you end up wasting food. Some fresh fruits and vegetables aren't available all year round. It isn't always convenient to shop at a roadside stand, so you don't always save money on fresh foods.

Editing

As a final step, Gus proofread his paper for errors in grammar, usage, spelling, and punctuation. Then he made a fresh copy to hand in.

Your Essay

Here is a good way to organize your writing when you are asked to write about the advantages and disadvantages of something. You can use it as a checklist to plan your essay and to evaluate it when you have finished.

☐ **1.** Decide on your topic.

☐ **2.** Make notes in two columns headed "Advantages" and "Disadvantages."

☐ **3.** Decide on an organization for your essay. The organization used in the sample essay in this lesson is a good one to follow:

continued...

Paragraph One: ADVANTAGES

- Most important advantage

- Next most important advantage

- Third most important advantage, etc.
  — with examples and details.

Paragraph Two: DISADVANTAGES

- Most important disadvantage

- Next most important disadvantage

- Third most important disadvantage, etc.
  —with examples and details.

☐ **4.** Decide how to organize your details. Which ones are most important? Which are less important?

☐ **5.** Write a draft of your paper. You may want to add explanatory details to some of your advantages and disadvantages. Remember that this is just your first try. You will have a chance to add, change, or take things out when you revise.

☐ **6.** Reread your paper and decide what you want to change. Make sure that each advantage and disadvantage is clearly stated. Check whether you have used words like *although* and *however* to emphasize any of the contrasts within a paragraph.

☐ **7.** Proofread your paper and correct errors in grammar, usage, spelling, and punctuation. Make a fresh copy.

3. Comparing and Contrasting Two Characters

Content Area: Literature
Resource Selection: "A Mother in Mannville," page 138

When constructing a work of fiction, authors frequently write about contrasting characters. Often they develop their characters in such a way that what one figure in the story does forms a contrast with what another character does. For this reason, comparison and contrast are common in writing about literature. In this lesson, you will work with a student who is comparing and contrasting two characters in a well-known short story.

Tina's Essay

Tina's class read the story "A Mother in Mannville," which begins on page 138 of this book. After they had discussed the story, the class was asked to write an essay on the following topic:

Responsibility is one of the themes, or main ideas, of this story. In what ways does Jerry show that he is a responsible person? Is the narrator also a responsible person? Compare and contrast her actions with Jerry's. Does she demonstrate as much responsibility as Jerry? More? Less?

Read "A Mother in Mannville" on p. 138, keeping the essay topic in mind. Then look at what Tina wrote.

Prewriting

First Tina took a close look at the essay topic. She decided there were probably four things she was being asked to do:

1. Show how Jerry demonstrates responsibility.

2. Show how the narrator does or does not demonstrate responsibility.

3. Describe how Jerry and the narrator are alike.

4. Describe how Jerry and the narrator are different.

Tina remembered the prewriting steps she had followed when she wrote her character sketch. This seemed like a good way to begin writing this essay, too. She read the story again and thought about the idea of responsibility. She remembered the day that she was supposed to fix dinner but forgot to go to the supermarket in time to get what she needed. It seemed to her that she had behaved like the narrator. She intended to be responsible, but she neglected part of the job.

Then Tina made two lists for herself. On one, she wrote all the details from the story that gave her clues to what Jerry is like. On the other, she wrote all the details from the story that gave her clues to what the narrator is like.

JERRY

quiet

doesn't ask for anything

decides what needs to be done & does it (storing wood, fixing things)

likes dogs

responsible for his own mistakes (ax handle)

does the job thoroughly—not just what's asked of him (feeding dog)

lonely

works hard—doesn't count the minutes—works until job is done

considerate—won't interrupt the narrator

NARRATOR

likes & appreciates Jerry (can tell from the way she describes him)

polite—pays Jerry, gives him gifts, spends time with him

wants to help Jerry—concerned about him

upset about Jerry's mother (angry at Jerry?)

doesn't like to be interrupted when she's working

doesn't really want responsibility for Jerry—relieved that he has a mother

doesn't take the time or trouble to find out the truth until too late

enjoys solitude

easier for her to go away and send a present than to stay and talk to Jerry

The next step was to put a check mark next to each detail that showed something about the character's sense of responsibility.

Complete this step for Tina by checking each detail in Tina's lists that could be used to answer the questions in the essay topic.

From her lists, Tina was able to arrive at a general statement about each character's sense of responsibility.

Complete these statements for Tina.

1. Jerry _____

_____ 2. The narrator _____

_____

Now it was time to turn these general statements and the details supporting them into the first draft of an essay.

Writing

Here is what Tina wrote. Notice how she used the details from her lists.

Tina's opening statement.

Tina describes Jerry's actions.

    In the story "A Mother in Mannville," the narrator admires a boy named Jerry because of his sense of responsibility. Jerry shows this quality in a lot of ways. When he comes to work for the narrator, he shows that he is not afraid of hard work. Even though he is small, he works as hard as a man. He doesn't have to be told what to do. He just sees what needs to be done, and he does it. For example, he knows what kind of wood to cut, and he figures out where to store it. He even fixes the path without being asked to.

Complete the following paragraph. Use details from Tina's notes and from the story.

Tina gives two specific examples of Jerry's sense of responsibility.

    Jerry demonstrates responsibility most of all in two situations. First, when _____

_____

_____

_____

The second time is when the narrator asks him to take care of her dog. _____

_____

_____

_____

_____

Tina makes a transition.

Tina describes the narrator's actions.

    The narrator is responsible in some ways, too. She pays Jerry fairly for his work and also gives him gifts. She sees that Jerry is lonely and lets him come visit her. Most of all, she likes and admires Jerry and seems to want to help him. The problem is that she doesn't really want to take full responsibility for Jerry. When Jerry tells her that he has a mother, she is relieved. She is angry at his mother for deserting him, but she is also glad that Jerry doesn't really need her. She can go away and send him a present, and she doesn't need to take the trouble of finding out what the truth is.

41

Revising

After Tina wrote this draft, she reread it to see whether she had done the following things:

Put a check mark next to each thing she did do.

1. Made a general statement about Jerry's sense of responsibility.

2. Backed up this statement with details that show Jerry's actions.

3. Made a general statement about the narrator's sense of responsibility.

4. Backed up this statement with details that show the narrator's actions.

5. Made one or more general statements that compare or contrast Jerry and the narrator.

Tina was worried about the last point on this checklist. She had not contrasted Jerry and the narrator. She decided to add a concluding paragraph that would contrast the two characters.

Write Tina's final paragraph for her. Use the groups of words given below to help you organize your ideas. Include both general statements and details that support those statements. Look again at the lists of details and the story before you decide what to write.

Jerry is _____

_____than the narrator.

When Jerry has a job to do, _____

_____

_____

_____

_____

The narrator, though, _____

_____

_____

_____

_____

Editing

As a final step, Tina proofread her essay and corrected errors in grammar, usage, spelling, and punctuation. Then she made a fresh copy to hand in.

Your Essay

You can use the following checklist to plan your essay and to evaluate it when you are asked to compare or contrast two characters in a story.

☐ **1.** Decide what questions you need to answer.

☐ **2.** If you can, think of something in your own life that makes the story clearer or more meaningful for you.

☐ **3.** Look for details in the story that tell you what each character did or said. On a piece of scratch paper, make a list for each character. Check the details that answer the questions in the topic you have been given.

☐ **4.** Decide on an organization for your essay. The organization of the sample essay in this lesson is a good one to follow:

Paragraph One

- Make a general statment about Character A, focusing on characteristics that he or she has in common with Character B.

- Add supporting details as necessary.

Paragraph Two

- Make a statement about Character B, focusing on characteristics that he or she shares with Character A.

- Add supporting details as necessary.

Paragraph Three

- Make a statement that contrasts the two characters and that points up their differences.

- Add supporting details about each character.

☐ **5.** Write a draft of your essay. Remember that this is just your first try. You will have a chance to add, change, or take things out when you revise.

☐ **6.** Reread your essay and decide what you want to change. Make especially sure that you included general statements about both characters, with details to back them up, and that you compared or contrasted the characters in some way.

☐ **7.** Proofread your essay and correct errors in grammar, usage, spelling, and punctuation. Make a fresh copy.

4. Comparing and Contrasting Two Events

Content Area: Social Studies, American History
Resource Selections: "The Virginia Colony," page 142
"The Massachusetts Colonies," page 144

In a social studies or history class, you may be asked to compare and contrast two events, two periods of time, two forms of government, two historical figures, or two places. Understanding similarities and differences is a key to understanding historical and social studies concepts, and is one of the main reasons for studying these subjects. In this chapter, you will work with comparing and contrasting two early settlements in North America.

Greg's Essay

In Greg's American history class the students read and discussed a description of how the thirteen colonies were begun in North America. (Some of the material they read begins on p. 142 and p. 144 of this book.) Then they were asked to write a short essay on the following topic:

> *Compare the way Virginia and Massachusetts were settled.*
> *How were these colonies alike at the start?*
> *How were they different?*
> *Base your answer on the information in this chapter.*

   Before you go any further in this chapter, read the selection "The Virginia Colony" that begins on page 142 of this book. Also read "The Massachusetts Colonies," which begins on page 144. As you read, think about how you would answer the questions Greg's class was given. Then look at what Greg wrote.

-------------------------- ❑ --------------------------

Prewriting

The chapters that Greg read contain a great deal of information about Massachusetts and Virginia. Greg saw a number of ways in which the two states could be compared. The first thing he needed to do was decide exactly what questions he had to answer. He re-read the assignment and then made the following list.

Complete items 2 and 4 in Greg's list.

   1.Describe the way Virginia was settled.

   2. Describe _____

   _____ .

3. Make a statement about how the two colonies were alike at the start.

4. Make a statement about _____
_____

Greg also decided that the words "settled" and "at the start" were a clue that he should focus on the very first months of these colonies. Although both chapters tell how Massachusetts and Virginia grew and changed, Greg ignored these details for now and concentrated instead on the early days of the two settlements.

To help himself think more clearly, he divided a sheet of paper into two columns. In one column, he made notes about how Virginia was settled. In the other, he made notes about how Massachusetts was settled.

Complete Greg's notes with details about the Pilgrims and Puritans.

VIRGINIA

Wanted to look for gold first, not build a settlement

Needed food and shelter

London Company owned the land— colonists worked for the company, were not shareholders

People who ran colony were in England, not in Virginia

Colonists not trained to survive; did not know how to farm or do other things for themselves

Bad weather—many died

Didn't learn from Indians—stole from them instead when supplies ran out

MASSACHUSETTS

Pilgrims—established independence from Plymouth Company

Came for religious freedom

_____

_____

_____

_____

Puritans—_____

_____

_____

_____

_____

_____

After Greg thought about what he had written, he saw that his lists contained some points that were alike for the two colonies and some points that were different. For example, he had "Bad weather—many died" on both lists, but he had different details about how the colonies were governed. To see what the similarities and differences were, Greg made a chart. He used the same details but organized them in a new way:

Add two more details to each of the four columns. Use Greg's notes, which you completed for him.

<u>ALIKE</u>

<u>MASSACHUSETTS</u>

Started by company in England

Bad weather (Plymouth)

_____

_____

<u>VIRGINIA</u>

Started by company in England

Bad weather

_____

_____

<u>DIFFERENT</u>

<u>MASSACHUSETTS</u>

Begun by farmers and craftspeople

Came for religious freedom

_____

_____

<u>VIRGINIA</u>

Begun by people not trained to survive

Came to look for gold

_____

_____

From this chart, Greg could make general statements about the similarities and differences between Massachusetts and Virginia. For example, he could write

Both were started by companies in England.

Both had bad weather.

Write two more general statements about the similarities between Massachusetts and Virginia. Use what you added to the "ALIKE" list, above.

_____

_____

Greg could also write

Different kinds of people began each colony.

The colonists came for different reasons.

Write two more general statements about the differences between Massachusetts and Virginia. Use what you added to the "DIFFERENT" list, above.

_____

_____

Now Greg felt ready to begin writing the first draft of his essay.

Writing

Here is what Greg wrote. Notice how he organized the details from his lists. How did he begin and end his essay? Is each paragraph equally strong?

Greg writes an introductory paragraph.

Virginia and Massachusetts were alike in some ways at the start. But they had different kinds of people in them, so they were also very different. They were more different than they were alike.

Greg describes how Virginia was settled.

Virginia was started first, by a company that sent settlers to Jamestown. Jamestown was near a swamp, and many people died because it was an unhealthy place. People also died in the first year because they didn't know how to do anything for themselves. They couldn't grow food, or build houses, or hunt. Many of them had come to look for gold. and they disliked the leader, Captain John Smith, that the company had appointed. But instead of trying to learn how to survive on their own, they wanted to wait for food to be sent from England. Sometimes they raided the Indians instead of growing or finding their own food.

Finish Greg's third paragraph, below. Use his notes and the selections from his American history book.

Greg describes how Massachusetts was settled, focusing particularly on details that contrast with the Virginia settlement.

Massachusetts had two groups of settlers. The first group was the Pilgrims. They came to this country because _____

_____

_____

_____

_____

The other group of Massachusetts settlers was the Puritans. Like the Pilgrims, they came to his country because they wanted to be free to practice their religion. The company that founded the colony was owned by the colonists themselves. They governed themselves instead of being governed from England, just like the Pilgrims did. The Puritans chose carefully who would go

47

to the New World. The colony had farmers, business people, and craftspeople in it, so that it could be self-
sufficient.

Write Greg's final paragraph for him. Use his notes about the differences between the colonies to guide you.

Greg sums up the important differences between the settlement of Virginia and Massachusetts.

_____

_____

_____

_____

_____

_____

_____

_____

Revising

Greg reread the draft of his essay to make sure he had done the following things.

Put a check mark next to each thing that Greg did successfully.

1. Gave a good opening description of the similarities between Virginia and Massachusetts.

2. Gave a good general description of how Virginia was settled.
   Backed up statements with details.

3. Gave a good general description of how Massachusetts was settled.
   Backed up statements with details.

4. Wrote a concluding statement that sums up the important contrasts between the early Virginia and Massachusetts settlements.

Greg decided that he had described the settlement of the two colonies in detail. And of course, you wrote a strong concluding paragraph for him.

One paragraph still needs work, though. Which one? _____

When Greg started writing, he wasn't entirely sure what he was going to say. As a result, his first paragraph has only vague general statements in it, with no details. Greg decided to rewrite this paragraph so that it would contain at least two ways in which the Virginia and Massachusetts settlements were similar. Here is part of his revised first paragraph.

Finish the revision for him. Use his notes as a guide.

```
Virginia and Massachusetts were alike in some ways at the start
```

_____

_____

_____

_____

```
But the two colonies had different kinds of people in them, so they
were also very different. They were more different than they were
alike.
```

Editing

As a final step, Greg proofread his essay for errors in grammar, usage, spelling, and punctuation. Then he made a fresh copy to hand in.

Your Essay

Reread the chapters on Virginia and Massachusetts from Greg's American history book. Then, on a separate sheet of paper, write three to five paragraphs on the following topic:

> *Compare the way Virginia and Massachusetts developed.*
> *How did the colonists live?*
> *How did they support themselves?*
> *Discuss both the similarities and the differences.*
> *Base your answer on the information in this chapter.*

Use the following checklist to plan your essay and to evaluate it when you have finished.

☐ **1.** Decide what questions you need to answer.

☐ **2.** Look for details in the chapter that describe the way of life that developed in Massachusetts and Virginia. On a piece of scratch paper, make a list for each colony.

☐ **3.** Try to reorganize the details you listed to show how the two colonies were alike and how they were different.

☐ **4.** Decide on an organization for your essay. The one outlined below may be helpful for you:

Paragraph One: SIMILARITIES

- Describe the ways in which the colonists' lives in Virginia and Massachusetts were similar.

- Give supporting details as necessary.

---

continued...

Paragraph Two: DIFFERENCES (VIRGINIA)

● Describe the special features that made the colonists' lives in Virginia different from those in Massachusetts.

● Give supporting details as necessary.

Paragraph Three: DIFFERENCES (MASSACHUSETTS)

● Describe what made the colonists' lives in Massachusetts different from those in Virginia.

● Give supporting details as necessary.

This organization is for a three-paragraph essay. You can make it longer by adding separate opening and concluding paragraphs, or by writing separate "Difference" paragraphs about the Plymouth and Massachusetts Bay colonies.

☐ **5.** Write a draft of your essay. Remember that this is just your first try. You will have a chance to add, change, or take things out when you revise.

☐ **6.** Reread your essay and decide what you want to change. Make especially sure that you included general statements comparing or contrasting the two colonies, with details to back them up.

☐ **7.** Proofread your essay and correct errors in grammar, usage, spelling, and punctuation. Make a fresh copy.

UNIT THREE: ANALYZING AND ORGANIZING

In most of the kinds of writing you do, you have to take a close look at what you are writing about, determine what is important about it, and decide how different pieces of information relate to each other. All this is called *analyzing*. Your next step is to arrange your information in some order that makes it clear to the reader. This is called *organizing*.

Without the steps of analyzing and organizing, your writing would be badly thought out and badly written. This unit will show you some of the different kinds of analyzing and organizing you can use in your writing. You will be working in the following content areas:

- Science

- Shop/Home Economics

- Social Studies/American History

- Literature

1. Describing Relationships

In nearly every piece of writing you will ever do, you will have to make clear the relationships among the various things you are writing about. You may have to describe events in time order, or put them in order of size or age. You may have to analyze events related by cause and effect. Or you may be concerned with a different kind of relationship—the relationship between characters in a work of literature, for example. This lesson will introduce you to the thinking skills you will use throughout this unit.

Sequence

Why is the **sequence**, or order, in which things are put together so important to us? One way of answering this question is to look at the two groups of numbers below. How is each group arranged? What does each arrangement tell you?

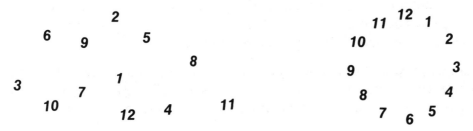

The numbers on the left are in **random order**. If someone threw a handful of numbers into the air and then made a picture of the way they fell, they might look like the numbers on the left. There is no meaning to the way they are arranged.

The numbers on the right are in a **sequence**—an order that has meaning. The numbers form a pattern—in this case, the pattern found on the face of a clock. The order in which the numbers are arranged, one after the other in a circle, enables us to tell time. We know that a clock hand will move to 1 before 2, or to 8 after 7.

Practice 1

What should the missing item be in each of these sequences?
Write or draw it in the blank.

Example: a   b   c   d   *e*   f

1.   2   4   6   _____   10   12

2.   ◯   ▭   ▭   ◯   ▭   ▭   ◯   ▭   ___   ◯

---

continued...

3. f   a ___ h   e   r

4.

5. Roses _____ red
Violets are blue

When one thing follows another in a clear pattern, we are often able to see more than just the individual items in the sequence. The whole arrangement takes on another meaning. For example, when the numbers 1 through 12 are arranged in a circle, we can do more than say which number will follow 7. We can see that the pattern is the face of a clock and that we can tell time by looking at it.

Look again at the example and questions of Practice 1, and think about these questions: How would you name or describe the pattern shown in the Example sequence? In the sequence in Question 1? In Question 3?

Practice 2

Number the items in each group to show what order you would put them in.

Example: Number the following items in order, from first to last.

1. Number the following items in order from heaviest to lightest.

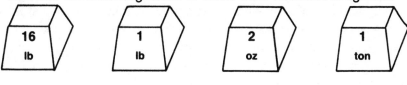

2. Number the following circles in order, from smallest to largest.

continued...

3. Number the following pictures in order, from oldest to youngest.

96 years   6 mos.   6 years   16 years

___   ___   ___   ___

4. Number the following items in order, from shortest to longest.

___   ___   ___   ___

Practice 3

For each sequence in Practice 2, write a general word that names or describes the order in which you arranged the items.

Example: first to last: <u>time</u>

1. heaviest to lightest: _____

2. smallest to largest: _____

3. oldest to youngest: _____

4. shortest to longest: _____

Sequence in Writing

Many kinds of writing depend on different kinds of sequence. When you tell a story, it is usually important to arrange the events in some kind of *time* order. Instructions for how to do something also need to be in time order. Even definitions, descriptions, and explanations can be organized according to an order of some sort—space order, or size order, or order of importance, or general to specific. The list could go on and on.

Deciding which kind of order makes the most sense for what you are writing is only part of the job, though. You also need to make sure that the order is clear to your readers. Words like the ones underlined below are called **signal words,** because they help the reader recognize the sequence.

TIME ORDER   <u>First</u> I measured the solution carefully. <u>Then</u> I poured half into one test tube and half into the other. <u>After a week</u> I checked both test tubes and noted the differences. My <u>final step</u> was to draw a conclusion about what had happened.

ORDER OF IMPORTANCE The <u>most striking</u> change was in the color of the solution. <u>Almost as interesting</u> was the fact that one test tube now contained less solution than the other. <u>Furthermore,</u> the one with less solution had a layer of tiny bubbles on the surface.

Practice 4

Each paragraph below is arranged in a different kind of order: time, general to specific, and order of importance. Rewrite each one, reversing the order. Remember to include signal words that will make the sequence clear for your readers.

(The events in the first paragraph are arranged in backwards time order, starting with the most recent event and ending with the earliest event. Rewrite this paragraph so that it begins with the earliest event and ends with the most recent one.)

1. Joseph has just started the tenth grade at Mount Valley High School. His family moved here from Rhode Island last week. Before that, he was a student at Sandersville High School. His earliest schooling was in Pennsylvania, at Pottstown Elementary School.

_____

_____

_____

_____

(The second paragraph starts with the most general statement and ends with the most specific statement. Rewrite this paragraph so that it starts with the most specific point and ends with the most general one.)

2. The best way to describe how Joseph feels about his new school is to say that he likes the feeling of independence he has. He has enjoyed making decisions on his own. In fact, his choice of courses was completely up to him. At Mount Valley High, Joseph was even able to pick the kind of English class he wanted to take.

_____

_____

_____

_____

_____

(The third paragraph states the most important reason first and the least important reason last. Rewrite this paragraph so that the least important reason is given first and the most important reason is last.)

continued...

3. The main reason Joseph's family moved here is that there were better job opportunities for his father. There were more jobs available for his mother, too. Almost as important is the fact that they could afford a house here. Finally, his family chose Mount Valley because the schools are good.

_____

_____

_____

_____

_____

Cause and Effect

When events in a story or steps in a process are arranged in time order, it is usually not difficult to understand the relationship between them. One thing comes before or after another. Certain events in a time sequence may have an additional sort of relationship, though. Compare the two sets of events below. Notice that there is another relationship implied in Example 2 in addition to the time relationship.

1. The Pilgrims were the first settlers to arrive in Massachusetts. The Puritans arrived next.

2. The Pilgrims were not able to practice their religion in England. They left England for Holland.

The events in both examples are connected by time. The first event happened before the second one. In Example 2, however, the events are also linked by a cause-and-effect relationship. The first event caused the second one. The second event was the effect, or result, of the first one. That relationship could be made even clearer if Example 2 were rewritten in one of these ways:

The Pilgrims were not able to practice their religion in England. As a result, they left England for Holland.

Because the Pilgrims were not able to practice their religion in England, they left England for Holland.

The Pilgrims left England for Holland because they were not able to practice their religion in England. _(Notice that the cause can sometimes be stated after the effect.)_

Be careful. There is a big difference between one event happening before another and one event causing another. Before you describe a sequence as cause and effect, make sure it really is. Often, the cause-and-effect relationship will be clear without a word like **so** to connect the events. If it is not clear, then use signal words like **because, so, therefore**, or **as a result** to make the connection. (These words are also a good way of testing to find out whether the relationship is one of cause and effect.)

Practice 5

Put a check mark next to each numbered item in which the sentences have a cause-and-effect relationship. (To test for cause and effect, mentally add the words "**As a result**" before the second sentence. If this makes good sense, there is a cause-and-effect relationship. If not, then the sentences do not express cause and effect.)

1. Louis D. Brandeis was a lawyer who fought for better conditions for workers. He became known as "the people's attorney."

2. Louis D. Brandeis practiced law in Boston. He later lived and worked in Washington, D.C.

3. The report was published in 1907. It described the terrible working conditions of women.

4. The report contained new and shocking information. It led to a change in the laws.

5. The steam engine uses heat to generate mechanical power. The first practical steam engine was built by James Watt in 1763.

6. The steam engine provided inexpensive power for ships, trains, and electric generators. Its invention is often described as the beginning of the Industrial Revolution.

Practice 6

Rewrite each pair of cause-and-effect sentences from Practice 5. Use one of the words or groups of words below to connect the sentences. (Remember that you don't always need words like these. The relationship is often clear without them.)

| because | so | consequently |
| therefore | so that | in order to |

1. _____

_____

_____

2. _____

_____

3. _____

_____

_____

Causal Chains

There is one more thing you need to know about cause-and-effect relationships. They don't always come in simple pairs. Sometimes one event causes another, and then the second event causes a third one. The second event is both the result of the first and the cause of the third. A *causal chain* like this can continue indefinitely. Here are some examples:

The steam drove the pistons.

The steam drove the pistons, which moved the crankshafts.

The steam drove the pistons, which moved the crankshafts that turned the ship's propellers.

Practice 7

Read the following paragraph. Write a C above each sentence or part of a sentence that states a cause. Write an E above each sentence or part of a sentence that states an effect. Remember that some sentences may be both effects and causes. Write both E and C above these.

When the shoreline of a lake recedes, bare rocks are exposed, creating a surface where lichens can grow. The rocks are also exposed to the weather. Wind and ice dig out bits of the rock, and dirt is able to accumulate in the cracks. Mosses and grasses, and eventually small shrubs, can take root in this dirt. The plants grow and shed their leaves, which decay and add another layer to the soil. Eventually the soil is deep enough and rich enough for trees to sprout where there once was water.

How many sentences or parts of sentences are both causes and effects?

(This is not an easy exercise, and different readers might find different causes and effects.)

Relationships Between Characters

You have been working with some patterns that show how things, events, or ideas are related. For example, things can be described in space order. You can connect events by putting them in time order or in a cause-and-effect relationship. And ideas can be arranged in order from general to specific or in order of importance.

Not all relationships you are asked to write about in school fall into the patterns we have discussed so far, though. When you are writing about literature, you are sometimes asked to analyze still another sort of relationship—the relationship between characters. The pattern in this kind of relationship is usually shown through the words and actions of the characters.

Here's an example. Read the following scene and think about how you would describe the relationship between Paul and Mr. Barnes. Look carefully at the words that tell what they do and say.

> Paul looked at the ground, shrinking like a timid mouse. "Excuse me," he whispered. "I didn't mean to disturb you." His hands shook slightly, and the cups on the tray he was carrying rattled.
>
> Mr. Barnes turned and stared without saying a word. Paul immediately felt as though he were an intruder.
>
> "I was just bringing the coffee you asked for," he explained anxiously.

Which of the following sentences best describes the relationship between Paul and Mr. Barnes? Base your answer on what you have read in this scene.

    a. Mr. Barnes is cruel to Paul.
    b. Paul is afraid of Mr. Barnes.
    c. Paul and Mr. Barnes do not like each other.
    d. Paul and Mr. Barnes enjoy working together.

The best choice is sentence *b*—Paul is afraid of Mr. Barnes. Nothing in the scene shows that they enjoy working together. Mr. Barnes may be cruel, and the two of them may not like each other, but the emphasis in this scene is on Paul's fearfulness. He shrinks like a timid mouse, his hands shake, he feels like an intruder, and he sounds anxious.

Practice 8

Here are two more scenes. After you read each one, put a check mark next to the sentence that best describes the relationship between the characters. Remember to base your analysis just on the words and actions given here.

1. "I'm first! I'm first!' " shrieked Betsy as she stuck her elbow into her brother's ribs in an effort to push him out of the way.

   "No!" Bobby protested. "I win—I beat you. Didn't I?" he added, turning to their father, into whose lap both children were trying to climb.

   "He's lying. And besides, he's stupid," Betsy said. "Don't listen to him. Listen to me."

   "No—me!" Bobby insisted. "She doesn't know anything. Listen to me."

continued...

   a. Betsy and Bobby are both afraid of what their father might say to them.

   b. Betsy and Bobby enjoy playing games with each other.

   c. Betsy and Bobby are in competition with each other.

   d. Betsy and Bobby have missed their father and are glad to see him again.

2. Trina was leading the pack when she heard the squeal and thud that meant someone had lost control and fallen. At the same moment, she realized that Jenny was missing. Her best friend and the only other cyclist as good as she was, Jenny was usually alongside Trina, challenging her with a grin. Sometimes one of them won, sometimes the other.

It must have been Jenny who had fallen, Trina thought. And then, without thinking, she pulled to one side, turned, and pedaled rapidly back to where Jenny lay, her lower leg at a funny angle. "You're hurt," she said, and swung off her bike.

   a. Trina cares more about Jenny than about winning.

   b. Jenny and Trina are determined to beat each other.

   c. Jenny is jealous of Trina's skill and luck.

   d. Jenny and Trina ignore each other as much as possible.

2. Summarizing a Process

Content Area: Science
Resource Selections: "The Respiratory System," page 146
"The Circulatory System," page 147

A process is an activity that has a purpose or a result, and that is made up of several changes or steps that usually happen in sequence, or time order. In this lesson, you will learn how to summarize and describe two natural processes: how we breathe and how the heart works.

Danny's Summary

In Danny's biology class, the students were reading descriptions of how the human body works. The resource material they were reading begins on page 146 of this book.

Turn to page 146 and read the selection for yourself before you go further in this lesson.

——————————————————— ❑ ———————————————————

As homework, the students in Danny's class were asked to write one paragraph in answer to this question:

How do we breathe?

As Danny read through the selection, he thought about what he would have to do to make the information fit into one paragraph.

Look at his reading material. To write only one paragraph that explains how we breathe, what would you have to do with the reading material? Write your answer here:

_____

To **summarize** or **condense** something you have read, you need to look for the main points and combine ideas as much as possible.

Prewriting

Danny knew that when you are describing a process—that is, explaining how something happened or how something is done—two things matter the most:

1. Making sure all the steps have been included.

2. Making sure all the steps are in the right order.

When Danny looked again at the selection, he saw that the first paragraph was mainly a discussion of a term, "diffusion," that did not apply to human beings. The second paragraph was a transition. The description of human respiration didn't begin until the third paragraph. Danny decided to look for the main idea of that paragraph and of the three paragraphs following it. Below are the notes he made.

Complete the third main idea in the list below.

1. Main idea: Chest muscle contracts and forces air to move in.

2. Main idea: Air moves from nose through throat and down windpipe into the alveoli in the lungs.

3. Main idea: _____

   _____

4. Main idea: Air containing carbon dioxide goes back same way and is exhaled.

Writing

Danny couldn't leave out anything important, but he could combine ideas and leave out some details in order to summarize the material. Here is the first draft of the paragraph he wrote. Ask yourself—Did he include everything he needed to? Is the order clear?

We breathe when the diaphragm contracts and air moves in from outside and into the nose. The oxygen from the air moves into the blood, and the carbon dioxide in the blood moves into the alveoli. That's after the air moves through the throat and through the windpipe and into the lungs. The air goes back the way it came and is exhaled.

Revising

Danny reread his paragraph to see whether he had included everything he needed to.

Reread the paragraph yourself. In the list below, put a check mark (√) next to everything that Danny did. Put an X mark next to anything that is missing from Danny's summary or that Danny needs to improve.

1. Included all the important points. (Check notes and textbook selection.)

2. Put all the steps in the right order.

3. Made the order of the steps clear for the reader.

4. Left out unimportant details.

One way to find out whether you have described a process well is to see whether someone else can understand it. In Danny's class, the students exchanged papers, and Danny's reader asked the following questions:

1. Where are the alveoli?

2. Does the air move into the throat, the windpipe, and the lungs all at the same time?

3. Shouldn't you reverse sentences 2 and 3?

4. How does the oxygen move into the blood?

5. What happens to the carbon dioxide after this?

While trying to condense the information in his textbook, Danny left out too much. He didn't always stick to what he wrote in his notes. Some of the essential details are missing. He also has some steps in the process out of order. He didn't use any signal words, and so he hasn't made the sequence clear enough. It's sometimes difficult to know from his summary in what order the steps of the process go.

What are some signal words that Danny might add to make the sequence clear? Write some examples here:

_____

_____

_____

Now rewrite Danny's paragraph. Keep as much of his original paragraph as you can. Only change what needs changing. Use his notes and the resource material to help you do the following things:

1. Get all the steps in the right order.

2. Make the order in which the air goes from throat to windpipe to lungs clearer. Use some of the words you listed above.

3. Mention where the alveoli are.

4. Explain more clearly how the oxygen moves into the blood.

5. Explain what happens to the carbon dioxide after it moves into the alveoli.

_____

_____

_____

_____

_____

_____

Here is the way Danny revised his paragraph. Compare your version to his.

We breathe when the diaphragm contracts and air moves in from outside and into the nose. Next, the air moves from the nose to the throat and then through the windpipe and into the alveoli, which are in the lungs. In the alveoli, the oxygen from the air changes places with the carbon dioxide in the blood. Then the air, with the carbon dioxide in it, goes back the way it came and is exhaled.

Editing

Danny's last step was to proofread his paragraph for errors in grammar, usage, spelling, and punctuation. Then he made a fresh copy to hand in.

Your Summary

Your assignment is to answer this question in one paragraph:

How does the human heart work?

Start by reading the resource material titled "The Circulatory System," starting on page 147. Look for the main idea of each paragraph in the selection. Then make notes that express these main ideas in one or two sentences.

Paragraph 1: _____

_____

_____

Paragraph 2: _____

_____

_____

Paragraph 3: _____

_____

_____

For a first draft of your summary, complete the paragraph below. Use your notes to guide you.

The heart is two pumps, _____

_____

_____

_____

_____

_____

continued...

_____

_____

_____

Now you should revise your paragraph. For a guide on what to do, refer back to the section on Revising earlier in this chapter, beginning on page 62. If possible, exchange papers with a classmate or work with a small group of other students and read your summaries out loud. Is the process that you are describing clear to all the readers or listeners? Have you done everything you needed to? If your revisions are minor, you may make them on the first draft of your summary. If they are extensive, you may want to rewrite your paragraph below:

_____

_____

_____

_____

_____

_____

_____

_____

_____

_____

_____

Proofread your paragraph for errors in grammar, usage, spelling, and punctuation. Make a fresh copy on a separate piece of paper.

3. Writing Directions and Instructions

Content Areas: Shop, Home Economics

Organizing a set of directions or instructions is in many ways like describing a process, which you worked with in the previous lesson. When you tell your readers how to make or do something, you have to analyze the task and break it down into steps arranged in time order, just as you do in writing about how a process takes place. In this lesson, you will work with two sets of instructions: instructions on how to fix a piece of furniture and a recipe telling how to cook a chicken dish.

Jay's Paragraph

In Jay's shop class, the students had spent the semester learning how to make different kinds of home repairs. They also read books and articles that explained how to fix things around the house. As part of a final project, they were asked to choose one kind of repair and to write a paragraph telling someone else how to make the same repair. Jay decided to describe how to fix a wobbly chair.

Prewriting

Jay was writing from his own experience in furniture repair, not from a book. His first step was to try to visualize everything he did when he repaired a chair, from start to finish. He sat with his eyes closed for a few minutes and imagined himself working on a chair. As he thought, he asked himself some questions. Two of Jay's questions are listed below.

What other questions does Jay need to think about? Fill in the two blanks.

1. What tools do I need before I start?
2. _____
3. What do I do next?
4. _____

Jay also thought about who these directions were for. He decided to write for someone who didn't know much about furniture repair.

How would the directions for someone who doesn't know anything at all about furniture repair differ from the directions for someone who knows a great deal about furniture repair?

_____

_____

Next, Jay made a list of the steps involved in fixing the chair. He wrote them down as he thought of them, in no particular order.

_____ Clean old glue off ends of rungs and legs and from inside holes

_____ Remove chair rungs and legs

_____ Tie rope around legs until glue dries

_____ Put rungs and legs back into holes

_____ Put on new glue

_____ Get together tools and materials (sandpaper, scraper, wood glue, a length of rope long enough to go around the chair legs)

Notice that this list doesn't include everything Jay will put in his paragraph. It doesn't say how to clean off the old glue or where to put the new glue. And it has one major defect. To be useful, it should show the order in which the steps are done.

Number the steps above to show the order they should go in.

Writing

When Jay was ready to write his paragraph, he added the details his readers would need in order to fix a wobbly chair themselves.

Complete Jay's paragraph for him. Use the numbered steps above.

To fix a wobbly chair, get together _____

_____.

To start, _____

_____. Next, you have to _____

_____

_____

_____.

As a last step, you tie a rope tightly around the legs and pull them together.

Revising

Jay looked again at some of the sets of directions the class had read that semester. Then he reread his paragraph and decided that he needed to add a sentence.

Put a check mark next to the sentence you think Jay needs to add to his directions:

1. A sentence at the beginning that explains what causes chairs to become wobbly.

2. A sentence between sentences 3 and 4 that explains different styles of chair legs.

3. A sentence at the end that explains how long the rope should be left on.

When you have decided what Jay needs to add, write the sentence in the proper place in the paragraph.

Editing

As a final step, Jay proofread his paper for errors in grammar, usage, spelling, and punctuation. Then he made a fresh copy to hand in.

Marlene's Paragraph

The students in Marlene's home economics class had read and tried a number of recipes. Their project now was to choose a dish and write instructions for preparing it that someone else could follow. The instructions had to be so precise and complete that another cook could create the exact same dish just by using the recipe—without asking questions or getting additional information.

Prewriting

Like Jay, Marlene was working from her own experience. She had decided to write instructions for a chicken dish she and her brother had invented. She had prepared this dish so many times, she could make it without thinking about it. So, without wasting any time, Marlene wrote out these instructions:

```
                    Summer Chicken
     This dish is served with rice. You slice some tomato and lemon. You
  put the chicken on a platter with the tomato and lemon around it.
  This is after you broil it for just 25 minutes, turning it once. But
  first you marinate the chicken breasts, after you remove the skin.
  Mix together plain yogurt, lemon juice, and lime juice with a little
  mustard powder, a lot of curry powder, and some pepper, too.
```

Because she didn't think or make notes ahead of time, Marlene ran into some trouble with her instructions. Could you follow her recipe easily?

What are the two main difficulties? Briefly describe them:

1. _____

2. _____

In order to begin writing, Marlene needs first of all to get the steps of the process in order. Look back at what she wrote.

Go back to Marlene's instructions, above and see if you can separate what she wrote into seven steps. Draw lines between the seven steps. Then number them. (HINT: Look for the seven verbs that name what you should do in each step.)

Writing

Write out the steps in Marlene's recipe by completing the sentences below.

To make "Summer Chicken," first, remove _____

_____.

Then, mix _____

_____.

Marinate _____

_____.

Broil _____

_____.

Meanwhile, slice _____

_____.

When the chicken is done, put _____

_____.

Serve _____.

Revising

Now that she had the steps in the right order, Marlene became aware of the second problem in her instructions. They are not complete. It would be difficult to make "Summer Chicken" from Marlene's recipe. How would you know how much chicken to use? Or how much yogurt?

Below is a list of ingredients. Many recipes begin with a list like this one. In some recipes, though, the ingredients are given along with the cooking instructions, not listed separately. Marlene has decided to use this second style.

Using the list of ingredients, revise Marlene's instructions by adding the missing information.

3 whole chicken breasts	1 teaspoon curry powder
1/2 cup plain yogurt	1/4 teaspoon ground pepper
2 teaspoons lemon juice	2 tomatoes
2 teaspoons lime juice	1 lemon
1/2 teaspoon mustard powder	

_____

_____

_____

_____

_____

_____

_____

_____

_____

_____

_____

Editing

As a final step, Marlene proofread her paragraph for errors in grammar, usage, spelling, and punctuation. Then she made a fresh copy to hand in.

Your Paragraph

Think of something you know how to do (perform a magic trick? fix a flat tire on a bicycle?) or something you know how to make (the world's best fried eggs? a knot that no one can untie?). Write a set of instructions that is complete and accurate enough for someone else to follow.

You can use the following checklist to plan your essay and to evaluate it when you have finished.

☐ **1.** Decide on your topic.

☐ **2.** Think about the steps involved in doing the task, and list them in the right order. Organize the list with a plan like this one.

> 1. List the tools and materials that are needed. (You may put these into an introductory paragraph, or mention them one at a time as they are used.)
>
> 2. Describe the first step (in time order).
>
> 3. Describe the second step.
>
> 4. Describe the third step, and so on in the correct order.
>
> 5. Describe the last step.
>
> 6. Describe any finishing touches.

☐ **3.** Turn your list into a paragraph or two, adding the details the reader will need to complete the task. Make sure you start by naming what you are going to do. Keep the steps in order.

☐ **4.** Reread your directions. Have you included all the steps? Is there enough information for the reader? Have you made the order of the steps clear by using words like *first* and *next*? Is there anything else you need to change or add?

☐ **5.** Proofread your paper and correct errors in grammar, usage, spelling, and punctuation. Make a fresh copy.

4. Explaining Causes and Effects

Content Area: Social Studies, American History
Resource Selection: "The Virginia Colony" page 142

Analyzing and organizing events that take place in a time sequence, the way you do when you describe a process or write instructions, is a fairly simple task. Identifying causes and effects, or chains of causes and effects, is a little harder. You must take care, not only in your analysis, but in your explanation—particularly where chains of causes are involved. In this lesson, you will analyze and explain some of the causes and effects at work during an important period of American history.

Diana's Essay

Diana is in the same social studies class as Greg, who wrote the essay about Virginia and Massachusetts that you worked with in Unit Two. Now the class is looking at the material again and discussing cause-and-effect relationships. The class has been asked to write a short essay on the following topic:

> *How did the physical environment of Virginia affect the development of the plantation system? Base your answers on the information in this chapter.*

Before you go any further in this lesson, reread the selection on "The Virginia Colony" from Diana's history book, beginning on page 142. Keep in mind the question that Diana must answer as you read the selection.

———————————————— ☐ ————————————————

When she thought about the topic, Diana realized that she was being asked to describe a cause-and-effect relationship.

Here are the two things Diana had to describe. Label them to show which is the cause and which is the effect.

The physical environment of Virginia _____

The way of life the plantation farmers developed in
Virginia _____

Diana also realized that she already knew some of the details to include. She knew, for example, that the Virginia colonists had developed large plantations. The part she hadn't thought about was what caused them to choose this way of life.

Look again at the resource material from Greg and Diana's American history book. Think about the details you remember from the essay you wrote earlier.

What additional kinds of details do you need in order to answer the question Diana's class has been given? Give one example here.

_____

_____

Prewriting

Diana knew that for every effect she described she would have to give a cause. So she decided to begin by making a list in two columns—*causes* and *effects*.

Fill in the blanks in her list.

CAUSES	EFFECTS
1. good soil and climate for tobacco	1. decided to grow tobacco
2. they needed lots of land to grow tobacco	2. _____
3. _____	3. slaves and indentured servants brought to Virginia
4. deep rivers	4. _____
5. _____	5. no large seaport towns
6. biggest plantations built along rivers	6. ships come directly to plantations

When Diana looked at her two lists, she saw that the causes and effects seemed to fall into two groups. One group dealt with causes and effects related to growing tobacco. Another group dealt with causes and effects related to the fact that the large plantations grew up along the rivers.

Diana decided to deal with her groups in order of importance. Since she felt that the decision to grow tobacco was the most important development, she put that first. The effect of the rivers and the lack of harbors on the way of life in Virginia, she felt, came second.

Next, Diana looked more closely at her list of causes and effects. She noticed three things about the list:

—*Some of her effects were also causes.* For example, her first effect, *Decided to grow tobacco*, was also a cause of *They needed lots of land to grow tobacco*. Diana spotted several other causal chains like this. (If you need to review causal chains, look again at Lesson 1 of this unit.)

—*Some causes had more than one effect.* The decision to grow tobacco led to a need for lots of labor as well as a need for lots of land.

—*Some effects had more than one cause.* The need to build plantations along rivers was caused both by the fact that the rivers could be used as roads and by the fact that there were no large seaport towns to serve the plantations.

Diana decided to make diagrams of her list that would show these more complicated relationships. She made a separate diagram for each of her two groups of causes and effects. Each cause had an arrow pointing to its effect or effects.

Here are Diana's diagrams. Fill in the blanks:

I.

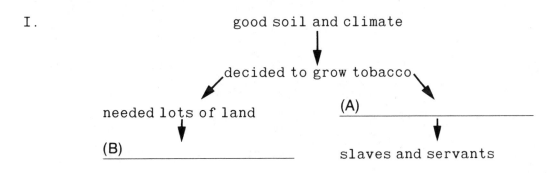

II.

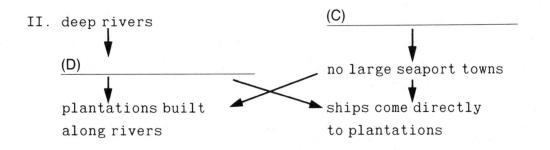

Looking over her diagrams, Diana noticed several things that would help her construct her essay:

—Each diagram would be a good paragraph.

—The cause at the top of each diagram was a general statement that would make a good topic sentence for that paragraph.

—The rest of the causes and effects in the diagrams were specific details that would fill out the paragraphs.

—The causes and effects in her Group II could be handled well in two paragraphs. The first would deal with the effects of Virginia's deep rivers. The second would discuss the effects of the lack of harbors along the Virginia seacoast.

Writing

Diana used her lists and her chart to help her write the following essay. As you read, notice whether she stuck to the plan she had made for organizing her essay.

Complete the first paragraph of Diana's essay. Use the details in her notes and her chart, as well as the resource material from the history text (page 142 in this book).

Diana discusses the most important set of causes and effects.

[1] Virginia has a mild climate. It also has good soil for growing tobacco. _____

_____

_____

_____

_____

_____

_____

This combination of large farms with lots of servants and slaves eventually grew to become huge, wealthy plantations.

Following her chart, Diana discusses the next most important set of causes and effects.

[2] Another reason that the plantation way of life developed is that Virginia had lots of rivers. They were deep, too. The plantations were like villages built along the rivers.

Diana uses the least important set of causes and effects as a conclusion.

[3] A final reason that affected plantation life was the lack of a good seaport town in Virginia. Plantations had to be built near rivers in order to trade with the ships that brought goods to them and that carried away their tobacco.

Revising

Diana made a list of four major points to check when she reread her essay. The first two points had to do with the content of her essay. The last two had to do with the organization.

1. Names all the causes, or conditions the colonists had found in the environment in Virginia.

2. Names all the results, or ways of life the colonists had developed in Virginia in response to the environment.

3. Describes the most important set of causes and effects first, the next most important set second, and the least important set last.

4. Within each paragraph, makes a general statement first, followed by specific details.

Then Diana reread her essay to make sure she had included everything in her diagrams and that the relationship between the causes and effects was clear.

Check Diana's diagrams. Look for anything she might have left out of her essay. See whether any of the cause-effect relationship need to be made clearer. Which paragraphs need to be revised or rewritten? _____

Diana realized that she had left out both some of the causes and some of the effects in Paragraphs 2 and 3. As a result, these two paragraphs were incomplete, and the relationships were unclear.

Which details from her diagrams did Diana need to add to Paragraph 2?

_____

_____

_____

_____

Rewrite the second paragraph of Diana's essay. Use the changes shown below, as well as Diana's notes and diagrams and the resource material.

[2] Another reason that the plantation way of life developed is that Virginia had lots of deep rivers that were good for transportation. _____

_____

_____

_____

_____

_____

_____ The plantations were like small villages. Each one did its own trading.

Now use Diana's notes and chart and the resource material to rewrite Paragraph 3. Follow these steps:

1. Begin with a general statement that mentions the lack of good harbors along the Virginia seacoast.

2. Tell what happened to the building of seaports as a result.

3. Explain the next step in this chain of causes and effects—the effect on where trading ships had to go.

4. Conclude by explaining where the plantation owners had to build their plantations in order to trade with the ships.

Rewrite the paragraph:

[3] _____

_____

_____

_____

_____

Editing

As a final step, Diana proofread her essay for errors in grammar, usage, spelling, and punctuation. Then she made a fresh copy to hand in.

Your Essay

Whenever you are asked to describe a cause-and-effect relationship, you can use the following checklist to plan your essay and to evaluate it when you have finished.

□ **1.** Make a list of causes and effects. List the causes in one column. List the effects in another column.

□ **2.** Look at your list for chains of causes, for causes that have more than one effect, and for effects with more than one cause. Make a chart or diagram to show these relationships.

□ **3.** Decide what kind of order you want to arrange your causes and effects in. Usually you will arrange them in order of importance.

□ **4.** Write a draft of your essay. Remember that this is just your first try. You will have a chance to add, change, or take things out when you revise.

□ **5.** Reread your essay. Compare it with your diagrams, and decide what you want to change. Make especially sure that you showed all the relationships between the causes and the effects, and that you described them in order.

□ **6.** Proofread your essay and correct errors in grammar, usage, spelling, and punctuation. Make a fresh copy.

5. Analyzing Relationships Between Characters

Content Area: Literature
Resource Selections: "The Sniper," by Liam O'Flaherty, page 148
"The Man He Killed," by Thomas Hardy, page 150

Up to now, you have been analyzing relationships between events and ideas. When you write about a work of literature, however, you must often analyze the relationships between people who are characters in the work, rather than the relationships between competing ideas or between events in a sequence. In this Lesson, you will analyze the relationships between people in a short story and in a poem.

Pam's Essay

Pam's class read "The Sniper" by Liam O'Flaherty, which begins on page 148 of this book. When they discussed the story, the students could see that it was about a very common type of relationship in literature—an **ambiguous** relationship, one that can be explained in more than one way. The two main characters are both alike and different. They seem to be enemies, but it is possible that they are not. The students were asked to write a short essay on the following topic:

What is the relationship between the two snipers in the story?

Read "The Sniper" yourself, on page 148 of this book. Think about how you would answer the question Pam's class was given.

---------------------------------- ❏ ----------------------------------

Prewriting

When she analyzed "The Sniper," Pam was reminded of the story "A Mother in Manville." In that story, the narrator wasn't always what she seemed to be. She seemed to take responsibility for Jerry, but she avoided a real commitment to him.

In "The Sniper," the two men are trying to kill each other, but the last line of the story says, "Then the sniper turned over the dead body and looked into his brother's face." Again, there is a contrast between what the characters seem to be and what they might actually be. Pam decided to focus on this last line and what it suggested about the relationship between the characters. She began by thinking about the meaning of the last line of the story. She decided that the line had two possible meanings.

What are the two possible meanings of the last line of "The Sniper"?

1. _____

_____

2. _____

_____

No matter how it is interpreted, the last line of the story indicates that the two men might be something other than simple enemies. So Pam's next step was to look for details that show the similarities between the two men. Here are the notes she made.

```
Both are snipers.

Both on the same street.

Both trying to kill each other.
```

Add as many details as you can to Pam's notes.

_____

_____

_____

Next, Pam wanted to see whether she could make some generalizations about the relationship between the two men. She based her generalizations on the details she had listed. Here is one of them.

```
1. The sniper and his enemy probably feel the same way.
```

Add another generalization based on the details in Pam's list.

```
2. _____
```

Writing

The two generalizations gave Pam main idea sentences for two paragraphs. This was enough for her to begin writing her essay. Notice how she used details to support her generalizations. Notice, too, the generalization that begins her second paragraph. Compare it to the one you wrote above.

Pam explains why she thinks the sniper and his enemy have the same feelings.

```
    The sniper and his enemy probably have many of the same
feelings. Each one thinks his side in the civil war is
right and the other side is wrong. Each one sees the oth-
er as the enemy. O'Flaherty says that the eyes of the Re-
publican sniper have "the cold gleam of the fanatic."
But the Free Stater is probably a fanatic too. He is also
on a rooftop in the middle of the night, shooting at
people.
```

Pam explains why she thinks the sniper and his enemy be-have the same way.

```
    The actions of both snipers are also the same. Each one
needs to kill the other in order to survive. Neither one
will give up. They are both very clever and very good
shots. They know how to stay hidden, and they know when
to shoot. The Free Stater is ahead for a while when he
```

wounds the Republican sniper. But the Republican tricks the Free Stater into thinking he is dead and kills the Free Stater.

Revising

Pam knew she needed to make some additions to her essay.

Check the three things that she needs most to add.

1. An opening paragraph that explains all the ways in which the two men are alike.

2. An explanation of why the two men were at war.

3. A statement near the beginning of the essay that describes the contradictions— the things that are not what they seem—in the relationship between the two men.

4. A paragraph that describes the ways in which the two men are different from each other.

5. A closing paragraph that tells what the sniper discovers at the end of the story.

Now revise Pam's essay by adding the missing elements.

Pam describes the contradictions in the relationship between the sniper and his enemy.

In the story "The Sniper," the two men are enemies, and so you think they must be very different. They ____

_____

_____

_____

However, O'Flaherty also suggests that the two men have a great deal in common.

Pam explains why she thinks the sniper and his enemy have the same feelings.

The sniper and his enemy probably have many of the same feelings. Each one thinks his side in the civil war is right and the other side is wrong. Each one sees the other as the enemy. O'Flaherty says that the eyes of the Republican sniper have "the cold gleam of the fanatic." But the Free Stater is probably a fanatic too. He is also on a rooftop in the middle of the night, shooting at people he can't see.

Pam explains why she thinks the sniper and his enemy behave the same way.

The actions of both snipers are also the same. Each one needs to kill the other in order to survive. Neither one will give up. They are both very clever and very good shots. They know how to stay hidden, and they know when to shoot. The Free Stater is ahead for a while when he wounds the Republican sniper. But the Republican

79

tricks the Free Stater into thinking he is dead and kills the Free Stater.

Pam concludes her essay by telling what the sniper discovered at the end of the story.

The feeling that the two men are the same underneath is even stronger at the end of the story. The Republican sniper feels curious about the man he killed. _____

_____

_____

_____

_____

Then, O'Flaherty says that "the sniper turned over the dead body and looked into his brother's face." They may or may not actually be brothers, but these two men thought, felt, and acted the same way.

Editing

As a final step, Pam proofread her essay for errors in grammar, usage, spelling, and punctuation. Then she made a fresh copy to hand in.

Your Essay

Read Thomas Hardy's poem "The Man He Killed" on page 150 of this book. For this assignment, think only about the story the poem tells. Here are some questions to help you in your reading and discussion of the poem:

1. Who are the two men in the poem?

2. How—under what circumstances—did the two men meet?

3. What happened between them?

4. How does the narrator feel about the other man? What connection does he see between them?

Then, on a separate sheet of paper, write a short essay that answers the following question:

How are the feelings the narrator expresses in this poem like those in the story "The Sniper"?

You can use the following checklist to plan your essay and to evaluate it when you have finished.

☐ **1.** Decide what clues to the relationship between the two men there are in the poem. Find the words and lines that describe how the two men acted toward one another. Find the words and lines that suggest another sort of relationship the two men might have had.

continued...

☐ **2.** Decide in what ways the feelings expressed about the two men in this poem are like the feelings about the two men in "The Sniper." Look for details that support your point of view.

☐ **3.** State two or three generalizations based on the details you have listed. For example, you might begin with a generalization like this: "This poem and 'The Sniper' are both about two men who seem to be enemies."

☐ **4.** Use each generalization as the main idea sentence of a paragraph in your essay. Use the details each generalization is based on to support the main idea.

☐ **5.** Remember that this draft of your essay is just a first try. You will have a chance to add, change, or take things out when you revise.

☐ **6.** Reread your essay and decide what you want to change. Make especially sure that you have a generalization and supporting details for each major point.

☐ **7.** Proofread your essay and correct errors in grammar, usage, spelling, and punctuation. Make a fresh copy.

UNIT FOUR: EXPRESSING OPINIONS

A very common type of writing that you should be able to do is the type given the general name **persuasive essay.** A persuasive essay may be your opinion of a work of literature, or an editorial, or even a Letter to the Editor of your local or school newspaper. In every case, your task is not only to give your opinion, but to state it in such a way that your readers may be persuaded to agree with you.

The purpose of this unit is to help you write convincing persuasive essays. You will be reading and writing in the following content areas:

- Literature

- Social Studies

- Career Education

1. Facts and Opinions

Facts and opinions—you use both when you are writing a persuasive essay. Yet many writers have difficulty distinguishing between the two. They back up their opinions with other opinions instead of with facts. Or they try to convince their readers with faulty thinking and faulty logic. This lesson will help you to become more aware of these problems and will introduce you to some of the right and wrong ways to make convincing statements.

Statements of Fact and Opinion

Are the following statements true?

> Abraham Lincoln was born in Kentucky.
>
> Hydrogen is an element.
>
> The dry climate of Wyoming has helped to preserve many fossils.
>
> New Mexico was settled by Europeans before Massachusetts was.

You may know the answers. But if you didn't, or you weren't sure, you could look up each of the statements in a reference book. (They are all true.)

Statements that can be checked are called **statements of fact.** Some statements of fact are true or correct; some are incorrect. The statement "Abraham Lincoln was the first American president" is an **incorrect statement of fact**. You probably already know that it is incorrect, but if you weren't sure, you could check the statement in an encyclopedia or history book.

When you read a statement, ask yourself if the statement can be verified or proved. If it can, you are probably dealing with a statement of fact. The next step is to check the statement to determine if it is correct or incorrect.

An **opinion** is a **statement of belief**. It cannot be verified or proved. There is no way to check it in a book or other library source. For example, suppose a friend calls U-2 the best rock band of the 1980's. Is this a statement of fact or a statement of belief? Ask yourself: Is there any way to check this statement so that everybody would agree? The answer is no. This statement is a statement of opinion, not fact. Some people might agree with it. Some people might disagree with it.

An opinion may be any one of the following:

> **A value judgement**, which states that something is good or bad or beautiful or ugly or the best or the worst. EXAMPLE: U-2 is the best band of the last decade.
>
> **A statement that there is too much or too little of something.** Matters of personal taste—too hot, too cold, not spicy enough, wishy-washy—are always opinions. So is saying that a story doesn't have enough realism or a movie doesn't have enough romance. "Too much" and "too little" can only be statements of fact when you are following directions on how to make or do something.

EXAMPLES: This oatmeal is too hot.

This weather is too cold.

This orange juice tastes too sweet.

A prediction. The future cannot be known for sure. Therefore, statements about the future can never be statements of fact at the time they are made. They are always statements of belief. They may become fact, but when they are first stated they are opinions.

EXAMPLES: Osgood Mackenzie will be our next president.

Sarah Jane Gomez will be a great success some day.

The Zoxil Company will sell more widgets next year.

Practice 1

A. Decide whether each sentence is a statement of fact or an opinion (a statement of belief). Write F for statement of fact and O for opinion.

1. ___Carla has been practicing for the marching band tryouts for two months now.

2. ___There are six spots open and twelve students are trying out.

3. ___Carla is going to have a tough time beating out all those other musicians.

4. ___Four of the musicians had places in last year's band.

5. ___Fortunately, she's the best trumpeter around.

6. ___She's been taking lessons for five years, and she plays in a band on weekends.

7. ___I think her chances are good.

B. Read each pair of sentences. Draw <u>one line</u> under the sentence that is a statement of fact. Draw <u>two lines</u> under the sentence that is a statement of belief.

1. The corner of Park and Chestnut Street is the most dangerous corner in this town. Last year, 14 pedestrians were injured there.

2. Juana saved $450 working at Allgood's Pharmacy every day after school. Part-time work is the best way to save for college.

3. "Angels from Nowhere" won two Grammy Awards last year. It's the greatest song I've ever heard.

4. Nora Kelly is the best candidate for Student Council President. As last year's class treasurer, she raised $200 for the class picnic.

5. It's going to be a long, hot summer. The temperature reached 95 last Thursday, and it's only May 2.

continued...

C. Which of these statements of fact are correct and which are incorrect? (You may know the answers to some of these without checking any outside source; others will have to be checked in reference books.) Write C for correct and I for incorrect.

1. ____It rained yesterday.

2. ____August 31 is your mother's birthday.

3. ____Albany is the capital of New York State.

4. ____The Mississippi is the longest river in the United States.

5. ____Koala bears eat only eucalyptus leaves.

6. ____H_2O is the chemical formula for salt.

7. ____The word *fact* is a proper noun.

8. ____The Dolphins won the SuperBowl last year.

9. ____The Civil War began on April 12, 1865.

10. ____William Shakespeare wrote *Romeo and Juliet*.

Valid and Invalid Opinions

Statements of fact can be correct or incorrect. But opinions are not statements of fact, and so we describe them differently. We say that an opinion is **valid** or **invalid**. A valid opinion—one that carries more weight and is more reasonable or persuasive—is backed up by supporting statements that are based on facts. An invalid opinion is not.

Imagine that Shirley and Janice, two baseball fans, are talking about their favorite players. Shirley says that Jack Casey is the best pitcher. Janice makes the same claim for Sandy Berra. Neither opinion is convincing at this point. Neither has much value. Each fan repeats her statement, this time with an explanation.

Shirley: Sandy Berra is the best pitcher in both leagues because he has the most strikeouts, has pitched the most innings, and won the most games.

Janice: Jack Casey is the best pitcher in both leagues because he has a really cool fastball, is great in nearly every game he plays, and is a better all-around pitcher than anyone else in either league.

Shirley's opinion is valid because it is backed up by facts.

Janice just adds more opinions.

Practice 2

A. Look back at Practice 1A again. Four of the sentences are statements of fact and three are statements of belief or opinions. Write each of the opinion sentences in one of the spaces provided. Then, after each opinion, write a fact sentence from the exercise that supports that opinion. If there is no fact in the exercise that supports an opinion, write "None."

1. OPINION: _____

_____

FACT: _____

_____

2. OPINION: _____

_____

FACT: _____

_____

3. OPINION: _____

_____

FACT: _____

_____

B. For each of the following opinions, list the kinds of facts that would make good supporting statements. The first one has been done as an example.

1. OPINION: Marta Hightower is the best dancer on Broadway today.

KINDS OF FACTS NEEDED: shows she has starred in

awards she has won

quotes from critics

what other dancers say

2. OPINION: We need more school dances.

KINDS OF FACTS NEEDED: _____

_____

_____

_____

continued...

3. OPINION: Everyone should take at least one computer course.

   KINDS OF FACTS NEEDED: _____

   _____

   _____

   _____

4. OPINION: Students shouldn't be allowed to work more than twelve hours a week during the school year.

   KINDS OF FACTS NEEDED: _____

   _____

   _____

   _____

5. OPINION: The best rock band of this year is _____.

   KINDS OF FACTS NEEDED: _____

   _____

   _____

   _____

C. Each of the following mini-editorials lacks a strong opinion statement. Read the editorial, then choose the opinion that makes the most sense and write it in the blank.

1. Ancestors of the American Indians walked across the Bering Strait from Russia to Alaska over 10,000 years ago. Small craft from Ireland may have found an American landfall as early as the ninth century. Viking explorers in the eleventh century landed on the shores of Canada. _____

   _____

   a. We should establish a new holiday—called Explorer's Day.

   b. Columbus wasn't important at all.

2. As part of a two-year trial program, football players have had to maintain a C average in major courses to remain eligible for the team. Our team won the championship last year, and our graduating football players are getting into good colleges. We have more pride and more team spirit, and no one talks about "dumb jocks" anymore. Now we have a problem. Tim Malone, our top scorer, seems to be flunking geometry.

   _____

   a. Let's make an exception in this case and waive the requirement.

   b. Let's keep the No Pass—No Play rule and get Tim a tutor.

continued...

3. Let's look at the facts. Military service after high school can be a good choice. You can earn money for college—the government matches each dollar you put into a special savings fund. You gain maturity—people depend on you. You can get training for a future profession. _____

_____

a. Everyone should have to serve in the Armed Forces.

b. High school juniors and seniors should think about going into the Armed Forces after they finish high school.

Faulty Thinking

Writing good opinion papers also involves avoiding faulty thinking. This kind of thinking is easy to fall into. Sometimes it is deliberately used to persuade you—ads often use it, for example. Nevertheless, it is not logical and should not be used in your writing. One kind of faulty thinking we have all been guilty of when we were younger goes like this:

Sal: How come you're not friends with Cal any more?

Mal: Because he's a jerk. (*opinion*)

Sal: What do you mean he's a jerk?

Mal: He acts like a jerk. (*opinion repeated*)

Sal: What does he do in particular?

Mal: He does dumb things. (*opinion repeated*)

Mal hasn't given any reason why he thinks Cal is a jerk; he's just repeated his opinion.

Here are some other examples of faulty thinking:

1. Bandwagon: It is human nature to want to avoid being different. This technique tries to persuade you to do something because everyone else is doing it. You are being asked to "jump on the bandwagon" with the others. The Bandwagon technique often makes a great ad, but it's bad logic and bad thinking.

Example: Have you sent in a subscription to your school magazine yet? More than 75% of the students already have. You don't want to be the only one without a copy. Send in your order now and be one of the Leaders and Readers in your class.

WATCH OUT FOR:

a. Phrases like "you don't want to be the only one without" or phrases that tell that a large percentage of people are doing or buying something.

b. Words indicating a group to which you belong or want to belong. The ad identifies the general group—students—and then indicates that students who subscribe belong to a special category of that group.

In the ad, what special group are you asked to belong to?

_____

2. *Unexpert Expert:* A person who is an expert in one field is not necessarily an expert in any other field.

Example: Stan Worsley, the famous comedian, says, "Take it from Stan. Your money works for you at the Second National Bank of Buffalo, Wyoming. Second Buffalo's trained money managers are tops in the nation. So if money means anything to you, go for the Second Buffalo! Would Stan lie to you?"

WATCH OUT FOR:

a. Opinions and recommendations from stars.

b. Words and titles like "doctor," "professor," "authority," if the so-called expert's credentials are not matched to the subject he or she is talking about.

What kind of expert would be a real expert on whether or not Second Buffalo was a good bank?

_____

3. *Faulty Cause:* This kind of fuzzy thinking is easy for anyone to do. One thing is not the cause of another just because one event follows another in sequence.

Example: Georgina had been warned. If she kept on reading romance novels, something bad would happen to her. Every week she bought a new one. By the end of the school year, she had read more than forty novels. She had also flunked three subjects.

WATCH OUT FOR:

a. Mixing up sequence and cause.

b. Both negative and positive uses of this kind of reasoning. If Georgina had got all A's, it would be just as "fuzzy" to give all the credit to reading romance novels.

What are some reasons why Georgina might have flunked?

_____

_____

_____

4. *Jumping to Conclusions:* Making a generalization on the basis of one or two examples produces this kind of faulty thinking.

Examples: Cats make terrible pets. You can't trust them. My aunt had a cat once that would leap at you and scratch you for no reason at all.

WATCH OUT FOR:

a. Generalizations based on one incident or set of facts.

b. Words like "once." By using this word the writer unconsciously tells you that he or she is generalizing from only one example.

From the information given, why do you think the writer doesn't like cats?

_____

5. *False Assumption:* The Bandwagon thinking error is based on the belief that if "everyone" is doing something, you should do it too. False assumptions usually spring from a belief that what "everyone" accepts as true is in fact true.

Example: Everyone knows that the rise in school dropouts is caused by watching too much television. If we can cut down on the amount of television that students watch, we can cut the dropout rate.

WATCH OUT FOR:

a. Statements that begin with "everyone knows."

b. Strong opening statements that are not backed up. The remaining statements may be logical, but the thinking is flawed if the opening statement cannot be proven.

What kinds of facts would be needed to prove the opening statement?

_____

_____

_____

Practice 3

In the blank at the end of each statement, identify the type of faulty thinking.

1. Cold fried chicken isn't good for you. Once my cousin Julius had some cold fried chicken at the town picnic and ended up in the hospital. You won't catch me eating cold fried chicken.

_____

2. Are you too full of life to be lonely? Are you waiting for your own Great Adventure to begin? Why not add your strength to the thousands of young people who have already put on Uncle Sam's uniform. Be a part of it—join the greatest team in the world.

_____

continued...

3. Andrew McCartney—America needs him. America needs a man who tells it like it is. Just the way he told you every night covering the city beat for MBC News. He's seen it all—the fires, the shootouts, the heartbreak—and helped you understand it every step of the way. Now get in step with McCartney—give him your vote—as our next Senator.

_____

4. Let Power Course put you in the big picture—right where you belong. But don't just listen to us—listen to Reasons. Here's the Reason why Mary S. Hart of Phillipsburg believes in the Power Course. "Power Course gave me all the confidence I needed. After just one Confidence Builder Lesson, I got the raise I wanted—without even asking for it. I can hardly wait to see what happens next."

_____

5. Everyone knows that Arco High cheats at basketball. They've won the division title for three years in a row, and they don't even have the top scorer in the league. Everyone knows that they must have bribed some officials.

_____

Practice 4

Write part of an ad or an editorial that contains one or more kinds of faulty thinking. Read it aloud or share it with a partner. Can your audience find the thinking errors?

_____

_____

_____

_____

_____

_____

2. Expressing Personal Reactions to a Poem

Content Area: Literature
Resource Selection: Ecclesiastes iii 1-8, in this chapter

In a literature class, you may be asked to take a poem and to write your opinion of it. For an assignment like this, the "facts" that support your opinion come from the words of the poem. These "facts" interact with your own personal experiences and feelings, and what should result is a new set of opinions and feelings that the poem has called up. This lesson will guide you through a student composition written about some famous verses from the Bible in preparation for your writing a similar composition about a poem of your choice.

Rita's Essay

Rita's class read the following verses from the Old Testament. They are from the book called Ecclesiastes.

To every thing there is a season

And a time to every purpose under heaven:

A time to be born, and a time to die

A time to plant, and a time to pluck up that which is planted

A time to kill, and a time to heal

A time to break down, and a time to build up

A time to weep, and a time to laugh

A time to mourn, and a time to dance

A time to cast away stones, and a time to gather stones together

A time to embrace, and a time to refrain from embracing

A time to get, and a time to lose

A time to keep, and a time to cast away

A time to rend, and a time to sew

A time to keep silence, and a time to speak

A time to love, and a time to hate

A time of war and a time of peace.

Rita's class read the verses aloud and talked about them before they were given this assignment:

What did you think of this selection? If you liked it, tell some of the reasons why you liked it. Mention not only the meaning but something about the way the words are put together.

Notice that Rita's teacher was asking for a personal response to the selection. Rita's opinion about the selection has to be more than a simple statement of how much she liked it or did not like it. She should show how she feels about it and give reasons for her feelings.

Read the verses in a whisper to yourself, so that you can hear what they sound like.

Write your first impression of the poem here. How do you feel about it?

_____

_____

Prewriting

Rita did several prewriting exercises to start her ideas flowing. First she made a list of some of the terms she might use to write about literature:

length	rhyme	rhythm
words	setting	dialogue
sound	plot	language
characters	idea	contrast
historical period	feelings	

Then she read the verses again and crossed out the terms she probably wouldn't use for this particular selection.

Draw a line through the terms that Rita probably won't use.

Next, Rita used a *focused writing technique* to help her find out how she felt about the selection. That is, she began with the sentence "These verses make me think about..." and continued writing for five minutes, focusing on the selection. She wrote every thought just as it came to her. She put each new thought on a separate line and didn't try to connect them.

Complete Rita's focused writing with some thoughts of your own.

—These verses make me think about a lot of things, like life and death, beginning and ending, dying and living.

—I like the rhythm. Each line begins the same way.

—There's no rhyme, but there is a lot of rhythm.

—It's like a drum beat.

—Everything is in opposites. For example, _____

_____

_____

_____

94

—I like it mainly because of _____.

—The words are simple and _____.

—Each line begins the same way.

—It reminds me of what my Mom said when my grandfather died—that the sadness was part of life.

—Everything has its own time. For example, _____

_____

—I think it's true.

—Always joins things by the word <u>and</u>.

Before Rita went any further, she wrote a couple of sentences that expressed what she felt. It would help her focus her thoughts as she wrote her paragraph. Here are Rita's sentences.

I liked this selection because it says something very true—that life is made up of opposites and that everything happens in its own time. I also like the way it says things.

Finally, Rita organized her notes and ideas under three headings.

Work with Rita's list. Add your own opinions. If you wish, feel free to disagree with what Rita wrote. Cross out anything of Rita's you want to.

RHYTHM	MEANING	FORM
repeating	opposites	each line begins the same way
like a drum beat	life/death	simple language
or like a _____	_____	_____
_____	_____	_____
_____	_____	_____
	true	
	everything in its time	

Writing

Using her notes and sentences to guide her, Rita wrote a first draft of her paragraph.

These verses from the Old Testament book Ecclesiastes express truths that we all know but sometimes don't think about. On the day of a party, for example, we don't like to think about an exam on the next day. And you can't think about life without knowing about death. Life is made up of opposites.

Even though there is no rhyme, the lines feel like poetry because they have such strong rhythm. Once you have read these verses two or three times, you cannot forget them. They begin to remind you of things in your own life—like the time my grandfather died.

The form is very simple. Every line begins with the words "A time to" followed by a word or phrase expressing an idea or an activity. The second part of the line also begins with "and," but this time it is followed by another idea or activity. Over and over again, until the reader finally understands. Everything that exists has an opposite.

Revising

When Rita looked at the first paragraph she had written, she decided that her first example was not a good one. She also thought that her last sentence might go earlier, and that she should give more examples from the selection. Here is how she started her revision of the first paragraph.

Complete the revision for her.

This poem from the Old Testament book "Ecclesiastes" expresses a truth that we all know but sometimes don't think about. It says that life is made up of opposites. For example, you can't think of life without death, or _____

_____

_____

_____ .

When Rita read the second paragraph again, she decided that she should add some sort of comparison or figure of speech to make her description of the rhythm more vivid. She also thought that the last sentence just didn't belong, and so she took it out.

Complete the revision of the second paragraph for her.

Even though there is no rhyme, the lines feel like poetry because they have such a strong rhythm. The rhythm is like_____

_____

_____

Once you have read these verses two or three times, you cannot forget them.

Rita thought the third paragraph needed more work. She needed to explain that the ideas in each line were opposites, and she wanted to quote one of her favorite lines as an example. She also needed to correct the sentence fragment that begins with the phrase "Over and over again..." She thought that she would do that by joining the last two sentences together.

Complete the revision for her.

The form is very simple. Every line begins with the words "A time to" followed by a word or phrase expressing an idea or activity. The second part of the line also begins with "and" but this time it is followed by an idea or activity that is _____

_____. For example, one of my favorite lines is [Write a line you like.] " _____

_____. "

This form is repeated_____

_____

When Rita read her revision, she was happy with what she had written, but when she looked back at her notes, she realized that she had not included anything about her own feelings or about how the selection affected her personally. She had taken out the reference to the death or her grandfather. She had also not commented on the first two lines of the poem. Rita wrote one more paragraph.

Complete her final paragraph.

One of the reasons that I particularly like this poem is that it re—minds me of _____.

My mother knew how broken up I was. She told me that_____

_____

_____.

I guess she was telling me what the writer of "Ecclesiastes" says:

_____

_____

Editing

As a final step, Rita proofread her essay and corrected errors in grammar, usage, spelling, and punctuation. Then she made a fresh copy to hand in.

Your Essay

Now it's your turn to say what you feel about a poem or a song. The poem can be something you just read yesterday; it can be something you learned years ago; it can be the lyrics of your favorite song. If you wish, you may write your own essay about the selection from Ecclesiastes. Whatever you choose, make sure that you care a lot about it. Good writing is never easy, but writing about something you love makes the hard part worth it.

You can use the following checklist to plan your essay and to evaluate it when you have finished.

☐ **1.** Get a copy of the song or poem and read it softly to yourself.

☐ **2.** Read it to someone else.

☐ **3.** Think about why you like the poem/song.

☐ **4.** Use focused writing (see p. 94) to get ideas.

☐ **5.** Group your ideas in some way that makes sense. Rita's organization is a good one to follow, but there are many others that are possible and that would be equally good.

☐ **6.** Write a general statement that explains how you feel about the poem and what you think it means. Include something about the language, rhythm, rhyme, or choice of words that pleases you.

☐ **7.** If it is appropriate, add a personal story that will help your reader understand why you like the poem.

3. Finding Thinking Errors

Content Area: Social Studies
Resource Selection: Fred Marcos's Letter, in this chapter

As you know, you are not the only person who has opinions. Everyone else in the world has opinions too, and many people write about them. Sometimes, what they write contains thinking errors. You should learn how to spot common thinking errors in persuasive writing, and how not to be fooled by them. This lesson will give you practice in looking for the thinking errors in a Letter to the Editor of a local newspaper, and will set you on the road to uncovering thinking errors in pieces of writing that you yourself find.

Todd's Paragraph

Todd's class had just finished studying some of the thinking errors people make when they express their opinions in writing. They had discussed all the thinking errors that you read about in the first lesson of this unit:

- Bandwagon

- Unexpert Expert

- Faulty Cause

- Jumping to Conclusions

- False Assumption

Then the class was given this assignment:

Read a local newspaper or a magazine that has Letters to the Editor. Choose one of the letters as a resource for a paragraph on faulty thinking. Write a paragraph analyzing the errors. The letter could be about something you agree with or disagree with— but it must contain thinking errors.

Read the Letter to the Editor that Todd chose, keeping the assignment in mind. The paragraphs have been numbered to make them easier to work with.

To the Editor:

1. I don't understand the uproar over the proposed new dress code for students in our schools. The arguments seem to me to be full of sound and fury and not much else. The Board of Education has asked a simple question, and we owe them the courtesy of a calm response. Instead, we have students marching in protest, social studies classes being used for debates on this issue, and entire school assembly periods being devoted to discussing the pros and cons of hats and hemlines.

2. I really don't see what the fuss is about, when everyone knows that dress codes improve test scores in every school that has tried them. Tieing a tie in the morning may not seem like much, but it concentrates the mind wonderfully. The student comes to school with a neat mind as well as a neat body.

3. When I was in school—and that was not too long ago—boys were required to wear ties and jackets. They could not wear sneakers or dungarees. Girls wore skirts and blouses or dresses and low-heeled shoes with socks. They never wore jeans or shorts. One girl who always complained about not being able to wear jeans to class left school after the sophomore year. She never could get any job better than stock clerk in the supermarket. That's what happens to students who don't care about themselves.

4. Dr. Ralph Carroll, the famous tree doctor, is one of the most respected professionals in this town. He knew what he was saying when he stated: "In my professional opinion, young people need discipline. Since they haven't got the desire to discipline themselves, they need rules that are easy to follow. Strict dress codes suc-

ceed where other kinds of rules fail because they are simple. No one can argue about whether a sweatshirt is really a jacket or a pair of short shorts is really a skirt."

5. Finally, let's look around us and see what other school systems are doing. San Gabriel, Bloomfield, Harwichport, and Massapequa have all adopted strict dress codes—finally. When they put in the new curriculum, they also decided to really shape up the students' bodies. And look at the results! State-wide test scores went up by 35% in the first year alone. Doesn't that tell us something? Or are we just going to ignore the success of everyone around us and be left behind like some dinosaur waiting to become extinct?

Fred Marcos

How many thinking errors did you find? Write the number. _____

Prewriting

Todd began by listing the sentences that contained thinking errors and explaining what was wrong with them.

Here are Todd's notes. Complete them by filling in the missing parts. Refer back to Lesson 1 whenever you have to.

```
Paragraph 2. False Assumption. "Everyone knows that dress codes
improve test scores. . . ." The writer gives no proof to support the
statement that "everyone knows."
```

Note that Todd uses ellipses (...) to show that he has left the sentence incomplete.

```
Paragraph 3. Jumping to Conclusions. "One girl who always com-
plained. . . . don't care about themselves." The word "one" gives
it away. The writer uses only one example—of a girl who didn't like
the dress code—and hopes the reader will believe that what happened
to this girl will happen to all students.
```

Now the ellipses show what is left out of the middle of a long quote.

```
Paragraph 4. Unexpert Expert. "Dr. Ralph Carroll, the famous tree
doctor. . . ."
```

[Explain how this is faulty thinking.]_____

_____

_____

Paragraph 5.

[Identify any thinking errors you find in this paragraph. Use Todd's notes above as a model.]_____

_____

_____

Todd felt that he had gathered enough detail to show that the writer had used faulty thinking. He decided to organize his paragraph by taking each point as it occurred. But first he wrote a general statement so that he could decide how he felt about the letter. Here is Todd's statement.

Fill in the missing parts for him. Use the notes above.

In this paragraph I will show that the letter writer's opinion should probably be ignored because it is based on too many thinking errors.

1. The writer begins with a false assumption.

2. _____

3. _____

4. The writer confuses sequence in time with cause and effect.

Writing

With his statement to guide him, Todd was ready to write a draft of his paragraph. Here is what he wrote.

Fill in whatever is missing. Use Todd's notes as a guide.

Todd begins with his conclusion and states his reaction to the letter.

The writer of this letter has strong feelings about having a dress code at the high school. However, his conclusions are based on such faulty thinking that his opinion is hardly worth considering. He begins with a statement that "everyone knows" that dress codes improve test scores. Since there is no evidence to back it up, this is a false assumption. Then, he jumps to conclusions by writing, _____

_____.

_____

_____.

_____

The writer's next thinking error occurs when he
quotes _____

_____ .

_____

_____ .

_____

_____ .

In the last paragraph, Mr. Marcos makes his final
thinking error: _____

_____

_____

_____

_____ .

Revising

Reread Mr. Marcos's Letter to the Editor. Then reread Todd's answer.

What paragraph of Mr. Marcos's letter is not mentioned in Todd's analysis? _____

In his first paragraph, Mr. Marcos complains that students are protesting, discussing, and debating the question of the dress code. He gives the impression that it is somehow wrong to protest. Todd happens to think that discussion and debate is a good part of what school is all about. He decides to write a final sentence to bring in this idea to give his paragraph a more interesting ending.

Finish the sentence for him.

From the first, Mr. Marcos seems puzzled by students who discuss,
debate, and question issues they consider important. Perhaps he
has forgotten that one of the very important lessons to be learned
in school is _____

_____

_____

_____ .

Editing

As a final step, Todd proofread his paragraph and corrected errors in grammar, usage, spelling, and punctuation. Then he made a fresh copy to hand in.

Your Assignment: Finding Thinking Errors

When you read something that expresses someone else's opinions, be on the lookout for thinking errors. Use this checklist to help you spot errors and help you correct the ones you might make.

☐ **1.** Does the writer talk about how "everyone else" is doing something?
REMEMBER: You don't have to jump on the bandwagon. Or jump off the roof. Or do anything you don't think is right, just because other people are doing it.

☐ **2.** Does the writer talk about how "everyone knows" something?
REMEMBER: Just because a lie is told loud and often doesn't mean that it's true. Ethnic and racial slurs fall into this category, and so do statements that begin, "Everyone knows you can't trust..."

☐ **3.** Does the writer base a conclusion on just one incident?
REMEMBER: Horses are not vicious just because one stepped on Vera's foot when she was little.

☐ **4.** Does the writer try to make you believe something by quoting an "expert"?
REMEMBER: In our legal system, a medical doctor cannot be called in as an expert witness about movie making unless the doctor also makes movies.

☐ **5.** Does the writer want you to think that the event that took place first is the cause of the second event?
REMEMBER: Superstition is based on false causes. If you rub a rabbit's foot and the sun shines, you might feel lucky. What will you feel if it rains?

Study newspapers, ads, magazines, and books this week. Listen to the radio and the TV. Find three examples of faulty thinking and list them here.

1. SOURCE: _____

   STATEMENT: _____

   WHAT'S WRONG WITH IT? _____

   _____

   _____

   _____

2. SOURCE: _____

   STATEMENT:_____

   WHAT'S WRONG WITH IT? _____

   _____

   _____

   _____

3. SOURCE: _____

   STATEMENT:_____

   WHAT'S WRONG WITH IT? _____

   _____

   _____

   _____

4. Writing an Editorial

Content Areas: Social Studies, Career Education
Resource Selection: "Horatio Alger Is Dead," page 151

When you have strong opinions or feelings about a topic, you may want to persuade others to agree with you. One way that this is often done is to write an editorial on the topic—in your school newspaper or in the form of a Letter to the Editor. In this lesson, you will first help a student compose an editorial on the subject of working after school. Then you will have the opportunity to write an editorial of your own, in the form of a Letter to the Editor, on a topic of your choosing.

Shara's Editorial

Shara's class read the article on page 151 about teenagers and part-time work.

Turn to page 151 and read the selection yourself before you go further in this lesson.

—————————————— ❏ ——————————————

Decide for yourself how you feel about the issues stated in the article you just read. Then imagine that the Board of Education agrees with the article and has the power to limit the number of hours students work. Write an editorial for your school paper, stating your position in the first paragraph. Then support your position with reasons and examples. Try to answer the objections of the other side. Watch out for faulty thinking!

Place a check beside the step that Shara must do first.

  1. Select good examples.

  2. Write convincingly.

  3. Form her own opinion.

Check the statement or statements in the list below that come closest to your own opinion.

  1. Students should not work part-time unless they have all A's.

  2. Schools cannot limit the number of hours a student works.

  3. Students' families should limit the number of hours the student is allowed to work.

  4. Students should be allowed to work as much as they want if their grades don't suffer.

So that you can understand Shara and help her write her essay, read this selection from a letter of recommendation that a teacher wrote about Shara last summer when she applied for a counsellor's job at the Town Day Camp.

. . . and in addition to being good with young people, Shara is a hard worker. She works at her studies and gets good grades even when the material is not easy for her. She also holds a part-time job during the school year and is probably saving for college. She doesn't spend all her money on herself, but helps out her family . . .

Write what you think Shara's opinion is about limiting the number of hours students can work part-time.

_____

Prewriting

Before she could begin planning her writing, Shara had to find out what she thought about the topic. She began with the sentence "I think it's stupid to limit part-time work." Then she crossed that out and wrote, "I don't think it's a good idea to limit students' part-time work." She continued writing for five minutes, putting every thought on a separate line.

- Rule is unfair to students who need to work

- Not school's job to control every aspect of students' lives

- Lots of jobs help with future career

- Some students earn money to help their family

- You can learn things you can't always learn in school

- Pay for music lessons or acting lessons or trips

- Angeline gives her mother $25 a week from her pay for groceries

- What about saving for college? Students don't just spend money on themselves

- Roberto started as a clerk and now manages the store on weekends

- Some students help out by paying for their own clothes and entertainment

- Jobs can help you learn good work habits

- Article talks about work being boring; what about school work?

Shara read over her list and put her comments about the benefits of part-time work into two groups.

Complete each list for her. You will find that there are three statements left over that do not belong in either list.

WHY STUDENTS WORK

Students earn money to help their families

_____

_____

_____

_____

PART—TIME WORK PREPARES YOU FOR THE FUTURE

Lots of jobs help with future career

_____

_____

_____

When she looked at the three statements that she didn't put into either of the two groups, she decided that two of them probably belonged together.

Put a check mark beside the two statements that could go into the same paragraph.

The rule is unfair to students who need to work

Not the school's job to control every aspect of student's lives

Article talks about work being boring—what about school work?

Next, Shara listed some of the reasons educators might object to part-time work. She used the article and her own experience to guide her.

Add two ideas from the article to the list Shara made.

Students with bad grades need to spend more time on studies

Some jobs encourage bad habits—like goofing off or cheating

Having too much money to spend can lead to drugs and alcohol abuse

Lots of part—time work is boring

_____

_____

Before she began writing, Shara made a chart to help her organize her thoughts.

I. Introduction

a. state the opposing position

b. state my position

II. Explain first reason with examples

III. Explain second reason with examples

IV. Answer objections

V. Conclusions

Writing

Shara used her lists and the chart she made to help her write the following essay. As you read, notice whether she stuck to the plan she had made for organizing her essay.

Shara states her position.

[1] I disagree with the proposed rule because it would be hard on students who don't have much money. Also, many students use the money they earn in high school to save for college or other courses they will take when they graduate. Finally, a good job can teach you many things and can help you prepare for the future.

Complete Paragraph 2 of Shara's essay. Use the details in her notes as well as the resource material.

Shara develops her first reason: many students need to work.

[2] Many students work because they need to work. They are interested in earning money, not just in spending money. Many students help their families by_____

_____

_____

_____

Other students _____

_____

_____

If they couldn't work more than 12 hours a week, they couldn't help their families make ends meet. Another large group works to save money. Their families may not need them to contribute to the weekly food budget or the clothing budget, but they need them to help out in other ways. For example, students can _____

_____.

Most important of all, _____

_____.

Complete the third paragraph for her, using the prewriting notes or your own experience.

Shara explains her second reason—the benefits of work.

[3] In addition to providing money for expenses and savings, a part-time job helps you _____

_____

_____

_____

_____ For example,

_____

_____

Complete the paragraph with a restatement of Shara's position.

Shara adds one final paragraph.

[Final Paragraph] Even if money weren't an issue, this would be a bad rule. People who object to part-time work for students don't know anything. This rule is against freedom and is un-American. It takes away the parents' right to bring up their children. Parents should have the final say about work and school. If a student starts doing poorly in school, the parents will know soon enough when report cards come in. They can then help the student make the right decision about balancing school

Shara summarizes her positions.

and work. To sum up, _____

_____

_____

_____

Revising

Shara made a list of three major points to check when she reread her essay. Two of the points had to do with the content of her essay, and one had to do with the style.

1. State my position and back it up with reasons and examples.

2. State the position of the other side and answer their objections.

3. Avoid faulty thinking.

Read Shara's essay. Based on the checklist she made, which paragraphs do you think need revising? _____

Shara realized that she had not stated the Board's position clearly in Paragraph 1. In addition, she felt that Paragraph 2 really covered two topics and should be broken into two paragraphs.

Next, she had not answered any of the objections to part-time work. The final paragraph also needed work. She felt that many of her statements were unnecessary and exaggerated.

Rewrite the first paragraph of Shara's essay. Use the forms suggested below as well as Shara's lists and the resource material.

[1] The Board of Education is considering a rule that would _____

_____ .

They feel that part-time work can be a problem for many students. It can lead to _____

_____

_____

_____ .

Although the Board thinks that these are good reasons to limit work, I disagree with this proposed rule because it would be hard on students who don't have much money. [The rest of the paragraph stays the same.]

Show where to break Paragraph 2 into two paragraphs by using the paragraph sign (¶) before the word that begins the new paragraph.

. . . If they couldn't work more than 12 hours a week, they couldn't help their families make ends meet. Another large group works to save money. Their families may not need them to contribute to the weekly food budget or the clothing budget, but they need them to help out in other ways . . .

Now read again the notes Shara made about why educators object to part-time work. Use them and facts and examples from the resource material to write Paragraph 4—a new paragraph that will come just before the final paragraph. Follow these steps.

1. Begin with a general statement indicating that the other side has some valid objections.

2. State one objection, using an example, if possible. Then answer the objection realistically.

3. State a second objection. Follow Step 2.

4. State a third objection. Follow Step 2.

5. Conclude with a statement that begins, "In spite of these objections, I think it is important not to limit students' right to work because..."

New Paragraph:

_____

_____

_____

_____

_____

_____

_____

_____

_____

_____

To help Shara eliminate the faulty thinking in the last paragraph, cross out the two sentences that make exaggerated statements:

[Final Paragraph] Even if money weren't an issue, this would be a bad rule. People who object to part-time work for students don't know anything. This rule is against freedom and is un-American. It takes away the parents' right to bring up their children. Parents should have the final say about work and school. If a student starts doing poorly in school, the parents will know soon enough when report cards come in. They can then help the student make the right decision about balancing school and work.

Editing

As a final step, Shara proofread her essay for errors in grammar, usage, spelling, and punctuation. Then she made a fresh copy to hand in.

Your Essay

Choose a problem that you feel strongly about. Write a Letter to the Editor of a local newspaper expressing your opinion. Here are some sample problems to choose from (or you may choose one of your own.) Whichever one you choose, do some research, get information, form a strong opinion, and back it up with facts.

The No Pass-No Play rule should be abolished.

Dress codes should be made stricter.

TV time should be limited to weekends only.

There should be ratings on rock lyrics as well as on movies.

Everybody who works the same hours at the same job should get the same minimum wage.

You can use the following checklist to plan your essay and to evaluate it when you have finished.

☐ **1.** State your opinion clearly.

☐ **2.** State the opposing opinion fairly.

☐ **3.** Devote at least one paragraph to each of your reasons for your opinion.

☐ **4.** Give examples or other evidence to support your reasons and statements.

☐ **5.** Try to imagine some of the arguments of the other side. Answer those arguments as best you can.

☐ **6.** Come to a final conclusion and restate your opinion.

☐ **7.** Reread your essay and decide what you want to change.

☐ **8.** Look for bad transitions, poor examples, not enough detail, and FAULTY THINKING!

☐ **9.** Proofread your essay and correct errors in grammar, usage, spelling, and punctuation. Make a fresh copy.

Note: If you have written about a problem that is of general interest in your community, send your editorial to the local newspaper as a Letter to the Editor.

UNIT FIVE: MAKING JUDGMENTS

How would you handle questions like these?

What do you think might happen next in a story? What evidence is there for your prediction?

Given a series of events, what do you think will happen next?

Which of several possible solutions to a problem do you think is best? Why?

The answers to all of these questions involve *making judgments.*

This unit will help you answer questions like the ones above by strengthening your natural ability to think in two important ways:

- Using evidence to draw conclusions

- Evaluating choices to make a decision

In this unit, you will be reading and writing in the following content areas:

- Literature

- Science

1. Drawing Conclusions

Much of the writing that people do, both in school and out, involves drawing conclusions from incomplete information. You may have to suggest a solution to a problem when you do not have all of the facts. You may have to guess at what is going on in the mind of a character in a story or a play, and to write about it. Whatever the assignment, it requires you to think carefully and logically; to draw upon your own background of knowledge and experience; to be creative in your judgments; and to use large amounts of common sense.

This lesson will give you practice in some of the different kinds of thinking skills you will use when doing the kind of writing that requires you to make judgments.

Making Inferences

You don't always need to have everything explained to you in order to understand what is happening. Your mind is very good at filling in the blanks. This kind of thinking is called **making inferences**, and you have been doing it since you started to think—right after you were born.

Practice 1

Which cartoon best fills in the blank in the cartoon strip? Circle the letter of the missing panel.

1.

 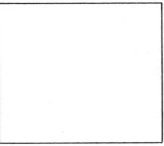 

Choices:

A.    B.

---

continued...

2.

Choices:

A.

B.

3.

Choices:

Now it's your turn. If you like to draw, sketch two cartoons—one showing a logical middle panel; the other an illogical one. If you don't like to draw, write what the panel should be.

A.

B.

You could have imagined an unusual incident to explain the final panel in each cartoon. For example, in the first panel, the dog's owner could have walked into the room and given the steak to the dog. Although this explanation is possible, it is not likely. It is much more likely that the dog took the steak.

Using Common Sense

Another good way to make choices is to use your **common sense.** This is the kind of knowledge that is based on experience—either your own or others. Common sense helps you know the right thing to do or say in many different situations. If you are a good observer, you learn by watching others and by listening to people who have experiences that you have not had.

Practice 2

What is the best thing to do in each of these situations? (Check the best solution for each situation.)

1. You have just taken a part-time clerical job in an advertising office. The first day on the job you wear one of the following outfits—jacket, tie, and shirt for males; jacket, skirt, and heels for females. Every other clerk wears sweaters, pants/jeans, and sneakers. You decide to—

   a. continue to dress up because you'll stand out in the crowd.

   b. dress like the others.

   c. dress any way you like.

2. A group of students from southern India are attending your school this semester. Two of them will stay in your home the month of September. You and your family are planning a cookout to introduce your guests to friends and neighbors, when you learn that your guests are vegetarians. To make them feel welcome, you and your parents decide to—

   a. cancel the party and take the guests to the theater instead.

   b. ask them to cook their own food.

   c. change the menu to an indoor buffet with different kinds of salads so that everyone has something they like.

3. You have volunteered to organize a fund-raiser for the gym team to help pay expenses to the state championship. You are a hard worker and want to succeed, but you've never run one before. The first thing you do is—

   a. go to the library and ask for a book on fund-raising.

   b. find out who ran the last successful fund-raiser and ask for advice.

   c. trust your instincts and make your own plans.

By using common sense, your own experience, and logic, you can make reasonable judgments. The conclusions you come to using these skills will help you select the best possible explanation or the best possible reason why something happened. Unless you see something actually happen, of course, you can never be 100% certain of all the facts, but your educated guess—or logical inference—will guide you to the most sensible evaluation.

Here's an example. Read the following sentences and try to think of what could go in the blank.

Darrell fell off a ladder while he was washing the second-floor windows.

_____

He didn't go to work for three weeks.

Which of the following sentences makes the most sense in the blank?

a. He decided to take a vacation.

b. He broke an arm or a leg.

c. He went out on strike.

The sentence that makes the most sense is *b: He broke an arm or a leg.*

Sentence *a* and sentence *c* are both possible explanations of why Darrell didn't go to work, but they do not follow logically from the sentence that tells you that Darrell fell off a ladder.

When you read a story or an article or a chapter in a text, you can rely on the fact that the writer wants to make the most sense. Sentence *a* would be a good choice to fill in the blank if the paragraph had been written this way:

Darrell won a round trip to Sydney, Australia.

He decided to take a vacation.

He didn't go to work for three weeks.

When you find the missing connection between thoughts or between sentences, you are making a logical inference.

Practice 3

In the blank, write the sentence that makes the most sense.

1. Nick had always wanted to play the guitar.

_____

By Christmas he could play ten pieces.

a. Nick listened to guitar records every night.
b. Nick took guitar lessons and practiced daily.
c. Nick was a good singer.

---

continued...

2. Pollution kills fish and trees.

_____

The trees and fish near Lake Goshawk are dying.

   a. Something may be polluting Lake Goshawk.
   b. There is a drought near Lake Goshawk.
   c. Developers have drained part of Lake Goshawk.

3. Acme Car Company lost money two years in a row.

_____

Two hundred workers lost their jobs.

   a. Acme closed one of its plants.
   b. Acme needed to hire better salesmen.
   c. Acme fired the president of the company.

Sometimes you can guess what happened at the beginning of a series of events. What do you think began this series of events?

Darrell went out on strike.

He didn't go to work for three weeks.

   a. Darrell's union voted against the new contract.

   b. Darrell fell off the ladder while he was washing the second floor windows.

   c. Darrell was looking for a new job.

The sentence that makes the most sense is _a. Darrell's union voted against the new contract_. It is the only sentence that has a logical connection to the rest of the paragraph.

Sentence _b_ could have happened. However, washing windows and going out on strike are not related in any way, so it is not a good choice. Sentence _c_ makes no sense at all.

Practice 4

Put a check mark before the sentence that makes the most sense in the blank.

1. _____

The colonists fought back.
The Revolutionary War began.

   a. The Declaration of Independence was signed.
   b. The British army opened fire on the American colonists.
   c. France was eager to help the American colonists.

continued...

2. _____

They made four runs in the last of the ninth.
At last, the championship was theirs.

   a. The Monties were behind by three runs going into the final inning.
   b. The Monties' pitcher was the best in the league.
   c. It was an unimportant game.

3. _____

The train was late.
She took a plane.

   a. Cora always took a bus.
   b. If the train was late, Cora would have to fly.
   c. Cora usually drove.

Practice 5

Read each paragraph and think about what is missing. Then check the sentence that make the most sense if you put it in the blank.

1. Charles, Erica, and Mark have planned a hiking trip. Although none of them likes getting up at dawn, the only bus that will take them to their favorite hiking spot leaves at six in the morning. They arrange to meet at the bus station the next day. _____

_____. Charles and Erica go on the hiking trip without Mark.

   a. Mark doesn't like the rain.
   b. Mark forgets to set his alarm clock.
   c. The bus doesn't leave on time.

2. Rosa doesn't like geometry—and isn't very good at it. Mr. Cedola, the geometry teacher, and Rosa's friends have noticed that she seems to be out sick whenever there's a test. On Friday morning Mr. Cedola tells the class to use the weekend to prepare for a test on Monday. At lunch on Friday, Rosa's friend Emma makes a prediction. She says: _____.

   a. "You're going to study hard this weekend."
   b. "We won't see you on Monday."
   c. "You're going to drop geometry."

3. _____ . They counted all the dead trees and shrubs. Then they analyzed the chemicals in the water. The park rangers told them about the decline in the numbers of birds in the area. All this had happened in the past ten years.

   a. The scientists agreed that the area was good for a national park.
   b. The scientists decided that the winters were too cold.
   c. The scientists were examining the effects of severe pollution.

Getting Additional Information

Recognizing when you need to know more about something is an important part of good thinking. Not even the world's best thinkers can make a good decision without enough information.

What additional information do you need to make this decision?

> Joe and Ted are going to the Drop Dead concert on Friday night at Green Stadium. The concert begins at 8 pm. There are buses to the stadium at 5:30, 6:30, and 7:30. What bus should they take?

What do they need to know in order to make a good decision?

1. How long the concert lasts.

2. How long it takes to walk to the bus stop.

3. How long the bus takes to get to the stadium.

The missing piece of information is the answer to Item 3—how long it takes the bus to get to the stadium. Once Joe and Ted know that, they can determine which is the best bus to take. Knowing how long it takes to walk to the bus stop can affect overall travel time, but has nothing to do with the choice of bus. After all, once you know that it takes 15 minutes to walk to the bus stop, you can leave early enough to get the bus at whatever time is necessary. Knowing how long the concert lasts is certainly interesting and may be important—especially if Joe and Ted have made arrangements to be picked up. However, this information has nothing to do with the question that is being asked.

Use your common sense, logic, and your own personal experience when you are asked to decide on something or to evaluate something.

Practice 6

Put a check mark before the letter of the item that represents the missing piece of information you need to solve a problem or to make a decision.

1. Kim wants to save to buy a stereo. She makes $30 a week at her after-school job and saves $6 of it every week. How long will it take her to save for the stereo? You need to know—

   a. How much she spends on her school lunch.
   b. How much she can make working overtime.
   c. How much the stereo costs.

continued...

120

2. Dave is applying for an after-school job. He is free to work on Tuesday, Thursday, and Saturday, but he is only allowed to work a total of 12 hours a week. He wonders whether the job advertised below would be right for him. What does he need to know to decide?

> PART-TIME SALES CLERK
> Kingway Drugs
> Weekdays and/or Weekends
> Minimum wage
> No experience necessary

   a. How many days he will be required to work per week.
   b. How many hours he will be required to work per week.
   c. How soon he will have to start working.

3. Jared is writing a paper on the causes of the Civil War. He makes a list of the causes he knows and finds articles and sections of books that discuss the war. When he has taken out three books, he wonders if he needs to find any more. What question should he ask himself?

   a. Have I got material on each of the causes I listed?
   b. How do I know that I have listed all the right causes?
   c. Have I looked at the assignment sheet?

2. Predicting the Outcome of a Story

Curriculum Area: Literature
Resource Selection: "August Heat," page 153

When you write about literature, you may be asked to predict the results of a character's actions, or to explain what you think happened in a story or a poem. To do this, you must make inferences and judgments from what the author has given you—and usually he or she has withheld important information for you to figure out yourself. This lesson will take you through the writing of a composition predicting the outcome of a story whose ending has been deliberately left hanging in midair.

Robert's Essay

Robert's class read the story "August Heat," which begins on page 153 of this book.

Before you go any further, turn to page 153 and read the story. Then continue with this chapter.

———————————— ◻ ————————————

When they had finished their reading, the students were asked to write an essay that answered the following question:

> What do you think happened to Withencroft and Atkinson after the ending of the story? Pay special attention to the clues provided by the drawing Withencroft made and the tombstone Atkinson carved.

On the basis of your first reading, decide what you think happened. Write your answer here:

_____

Then look at what Robert wrote in his prewriting notes below.

Prewriting

Robert's job was to arrive at a conclusion that had not been stated in the story.

What does Robert's conclusion have to be based on?

_____

_____

To begin, Robert used his first impressions of the story to make a preliminary judgment:

    Atkinson murders Withencroft.

With his preliminary judgment in mind, Robert read the story a second time. This time, he made a list of all the details that supported his judgment, including the clues that were mentioned in the essay assignment.

Here are Robert's notes. Complete them by filling the blanks with details from the story.

    Tombstone Atkinson carved:

    —Withencroft's name on it

    —date of Withencroft's birth

    —_____

    _____

    Drawing Withencroft made:

    —seems to be a portrait of Atkinson

    —expression of _____.

    —_____

    _____

    Atkinson's tools:

    —_____

    _____

    —_____

    _____

    Hints in the weather that something strange is going to happen:

    —_____

    _____

    —_____

    _____

    Narrator's language at end of story:

    —use of present tense

    —"I shall be gone in less than an hour."

Robert felt that the details he listed all supported his preliminary conclusion: that Atkinson murders Withencroft after the end of the story. Now he needed some way to organize his evidence. He decided to write a statement explaining what he intended to do in his essay. This would help him see how to organize the essay. It would also show him whether he had answered the question completely. Here is Robert's statement.

Fill in the missing parts for him. Use his prewriting notes to guide you.

In this essay I will use the following evidence to show that the author of "August Heat" implies that Atkinson murders Withencroft:

1. Withencroft's portrait of Atkinson

2. _____

3. The extremely hot weather

4. _____

5. The fact that the narrator leaves the story unfinished

Writing

With his statement to guide him, Robert was ready to write a first draft of his essay. Here is what he wrote. Notice what kinds of general statements he made.

Robert states his conclusion and makes a generalization about what it is based on.

The story "August Heat" by W. F. Harvey ends without telling the reader what happened. However, the author implies a great deal. There is a lot of evidence in the story that the character named Atkinson is going to murder the narrator (Withencroft). In this essay, I will explain how the evidence supports this conclusion.

Robert explains the first major piece of evidence: the drawing.

In the first place, Withencroft has drawn an imaginary scene. It shows _____

_____ When Withencroft meets Atkinson,

he realizes that _____

_____

_____

So this drawing could suggest _____.

_____

Complete this paragraph. Use the story and Robert's notes.

Robert explains the second major piece of evidence: the tombstone.

In the same way, Atkinson has carved an inscription on a tombstone, using a name that just came into his head.

_____

_____

_____

_____

_____

_____

_____

Robert explains two smaller pieces of evidence: the weather and the tools.

The strange atmosphere of the story is also helped by

_____

_____

_____ . The last two lines of the story—" _____

_____ "—could mean that _____

_____ .

In addition, Atkinson has just finished _____ .

_____

_____ .

Revising

Reread Robert's essay. Did he include everything he listed in the statement explaining what he intended to do in this essay?

Put a check mark next to everything in Robert's statement (at the end of the Prewriting section) that he included in the essay. What does he still need to add to the essay?

_____

Robert's essay doesn't have a strong ending. Since he still has one more piece of evidence to discuss, he could use that as a conclusion for his essay. Here is part of his concluding paragraph.

Finish the paragraph for Robert. Use the story and his notes.

The final piece of evidence is the fact that the story ends before the action is finished. Withencroft is describing the scene. You know that he is writing things as they happen, and not afterwards, because he _____

_____ .

The whole scene, with the heat building up, a storm about to happen, and Atkinson sharpening his tools, seems to be leading up to _____

_____ .

Withencroft says, "I shall be gone in less than an hour," but he doesn't tell us what happened after he left. The only conclusion you can draw is _____ .

Editing

As a final step, Robert proofread his essay and corrected errors in grammar, usage, spelling, and punctuation. Then he made a fresh copy to hand in.

Your Essay

The following steps sum up one way to organize an essay when you are asked to explain things that an author has implied but not stated.

☐ **1.** Read the story once and draw a preliminary conclusion.

☐ **2.** Reread the story, looking for evidence to support your conclusion. Make a list of these details.

☐ **3.** Write some statements outlining what you intend to do in your essay. You can use a framework like this one:

> In this essay, I will use the following evidence to show that _____ :
>
> ● (First major piece of evidence) _____
>
> ● (Second major piece of evidence) _____
>
> ● (Other evidence) _____

Use these statements to help you organize your essay.

☐ **4.** Write a draft of your essay. Remember that this is just your first try. You will have a chance to add, change, or take things out when you revise.

☐ **5.** Reread your essay. Check what you have written against the statement explaining what you intended to do in your essay. Add or change whatever you need to.

☐ **6.** Proofread your essay and correct errors in grammar, usage, spelling, and punctuation. Make a fresh copy.

3. *Suggesting Solutions for Problems*

Curriculum Area: Science
Resource Selections: "No Place to Throw It," page 156
"Warming Up the World," page 158

Whenever a problem comes up in government or a business, whoever is in charge usually asks for what is called a "position paper" about it. A position paper looks at the problem, reviews possible solutions, and comes up with a recommendation. It is a very common kind of writing, and it requires the writer to be both careful and creative in his or her judgments. This lesson will guide you through position papers on two current problems involving the trash we create and the atmosphere that controls the world's climate.

Lola's Essay

Lola's class read and discussed the article "No Place to Throw It," about trash disposal, which begins on page 156 of this book. Then the students were asked to write an essay that answered the following questions:

> *What are some of the problems associated with trash and waste disposal today? What are some of the solutions to these problems? Write an essay in which you define the problem, and discuss the pros and cons of at least two solutions. Then decide on a course of action that you think is reasonable and describe it. Imagine that you are the engineering aide to the governor of your state and write the paper with that in mind.*

Before you go any further in this lesson, turn to page 156 and read the article with this assignment in mind.

——————————————— □ ———————————————

Write the solution proposed in the article that seems to make the most sense to you.

_____

Prewriting

Lola's job was to think about possible solutions to the problem of trash/waste disposal. In order to do this she had to go beyond what was in the article. But first, to make sure she understood what the article said, she drew up a rough outline of what she had read.

Complete the outline by taking the facts from the article.

Problem: Getting rid of trash/waste

What is Trash? Trash is sold waste. It is made up of _____

_____

Why Is it a Problem? _____

_____

Current Disposal Methods and Their Drawbacks

1. Landfill—reaching capacity and closing down at a rapid rate

2. Burning—_____

3. Recycling—doesn't take care of all the trash; hard to get everybody to do it

Possible Solutions

1. Creating new landfill

2. Better and cleaner incineration

3. _____

4. _____

After she had finished, Lola thought about what she would recommend. She would put her recommendation in the final paragraph.

Write your own recommendation on the lines below.

_____

_____

Before she began writing, Lola needed to turn her reader's outline into a writer's outline.

Complete her outline with information from the article you have read.

I. Opening

   state problem

   define trash and give examples

II. Method 1: _____

_____

   people in emptier states don't want other people's trash

   landfills need to be guarded

128

III. _____

burning causes air pollution

_____

recycling needs to be enforced

IV. Recommendations

make landfills pay

make recycling work

_____

_____

Writing

In the first paragraph, Lola began by defining trash.

Complete the paragraph with what you have learned from reading the article.

Lola defines the problem.

[1] One of the biggest problems we face in America today is right in our own backyards. The problem is trash —and what to do with it. The trash we produce is made up of a lot of everyday things. Most of it is made up of _____.

_____.

The rest of the trash is anything else that people throw away.

Next, Lola described the first method and its drawbacks.

Complete the paragraph, using the outline and the article.

Lola describes one method and its problems.

[2] There have always been two standard methods of getting rid of trash. Up till now they have worked fairly well. The first method, dumping, is one that people have used throughout history. Trash is collected and taken to _____

_____.

But in the crowded cities of the Northeast and West, there is no more space left. What about sending trash to the wide open spaces in the West? ____

_____

_____.

Also, landfills present another problem. _____

129

_____

_____.

Following her outline, Lola wrote the next section.

Complete this paragraph, using the outline and the article.

Lola describes the second method, noting the problems.

[3] Burning trash is also an ancient way of getting rid of waste. However, we have learned that burning wastes can cause air pollution. Most cities that depended on incineration have had to abandon this method since the Clean Air Act of 1970 was passed. To make burning safe, we would need to develop ___

_____.

But even if we did this, _____

_____

_____.

Complete Lola's final paragraph. Add a solution of your own.

Lola gives possible solutions in the final paragraph.

[4] How can this problem be solved? One way would be to encourage communities to build more efficient, European-style incinerators. To cut down on pollution even more, trash would have to be separated before it was burned. People who didn't separate their trash would have to pay more taxes or be fined. [Add your solution here. Have you thought about landfills?]

_____

_____.

_____.

Perhaps we can solve our problems by doing something totally different and unexpected, like producing less trash. Manufacturers would cut down on extra packaging if they had to pay a packaging tax. At first they would pass the tax along to the buyer by raising the price. But eventually another manufacturer would produce the same item with less packaging for less money and buyers would switch brands.

Revising

Lola decided she wanted to make some additions and changes in her draft.

In Paragraph 1, using the article and her own experience, Lola decided to add specific examples for each of the major kinds of trash mentioned—paper, glass, and plastics. She wanted her reader to recognize that everyone contributed to this problem of trash, so she chose some examples that would mean something to students. As an example of paper trash, she thought of candy and snack wrappers. She also decided to add the percentages of each kind of trash.

Complete the revision for Lola.

> . . . Most of it is made up of paper, glass, and plastic. Paper trash, which makes up thirty-seven percent of the total, includes everything from newspapers to candy and snack wrappers. _____
>
> _____
>
> _____
>
> _____

In Paragraph 2 Lola wanted to support her statement that there is no more space left by using specific examples. She reread the article and found some interesting information about the number of landfills in New York State and the size of the Fresh Kills landfill.

Write the sentence that she needs to support her statement.

> . . . there is no more space left. In New York State, for example, ___
>
> _____
>
> _____
>
> _____

After she made this change, Lola decided Paragraph 2 was too long.

Put a (¶) at the beginning of the sentence in Paragraph 2 that will start a new paragraph.

In Paragraph 3, Lola realized that she had forgotten to write about enforcing recycling.

Complete the revision for Lola.

> . . . we would still have the problem of separating the burnables. One way to do this _____
>
> _____
>
> _____
>
> _____

Finally, Lola wanted to add a sentence at the very end that would sum up all her suggestions. She wanted to make it very clear that no one thing would solve the problem. Only a combination of solutions would work.

Write a summing up-sentence for the last paragraph.

> _____
>
> _____

Editing

As a final step, Lola proofread her essay for errors in grammar, usage, spelling, and punctuation. Then she made a fresh copy to hand in.

Your Essay

Read the article "Warming Up the World," on page 158 of this book. Then write a paper that describes the problem discussed, evaluates some possible solutions, and concludes with your recommendation.

You can use the following checklist to plan your essay and to evaluate it when you have finished.

☐ **1.** Analyze the paper you have read by making a reader's outline.

☐ **2.** Think about possible solutions and write one sentence telling what you would do. This is your general statement.

☐ **3.** Decide on an organization for your essay. The one outlined below may be of help to you:

Paragraph One

- State the overall problem.

- Give examples and details as necessary

Paragraphs Two and Three

- Describe one way of handling a problem. Discuss the advantages of handling it this way.

Paragraphs Three and Four

- Describe another way of handling the problem. Discuss the advantages of handling it this way.

Paragraph Five

- Evaluate the solutions and make a judgment. Finish with a summing-up sentence.

☐ **4.** Write a draft of your essay. Remember that this is just your first try. You will have a chance to add, change, or take out things when you revise.

☐ **5.** Read your draft and decide what you want to change or add. Look for places where you can add more detail or examples. Look for places where your language or thought can be made clearer.

☐ **6.** Proofread your essay and correct errors in grammar, usage, spelling, and punctuation. Make a fresh copy.

Note: Ask your science teacher if you may submit this paper for extra credit.

READING SELECTIONS

How Anansi Stole All the Wisdom in the World

[One of the most famous heroes in African folk tales is Anansi (uh-NAN-see), the spider who can take the shape of a man. He is not the usual kind of hero, though, as you will learn from this story.]

Anansi Spider was happy. He had tricked the forest god into giving him the power of changing himself into a man whenever he wanted. Now he had a wife and a son, a vegetable patch, and a good hut that kept out all the rain. When he wanted to hide or play tricks on the animals, he changed back into a spider, but when he wanted to relax and enjoy all that he had won for himself, he became a man. ''I much prefer,'' thought Anansi, ''eating meat and fruit, to eating insects. On the other hand, spinning a silk thread and swinging from the trees as gracefully as a bird is easier than climbing. Then again, having hands to hold things is a lot better than trying to hold things with your mouth . . .'' And so he went, telling himself what a good life he had now that he could be any shape he wanted.

One day, though, Anansi felt restless. He had had enough of sitting back and thinking what fun it was to be Anansi. He looked around him and saw all the village people working hard to make their crops grow; the bees were buzzing busily around the flowers, sipping nectar that they could turn into honey; the leopard was showing her kits how to crack open the leg bone of a deer. Everyone was busy, including his son Kweku, who was such a good carver of gourds that people came from miles around to buy his pots.

But Anansi did not want to work. He preferred to get things by trickery. If only he had something to sell. If only he had something to sell that he didn't have to buy. If only he could take something from the people and the animals so secretly and stealthily that they didn't know what he was doing — then sell it back to them, one piece at a time. He would be so rich he would never have to work.

And that was the day Anansi decided to steal all the wisdom in the world.

But first he would need a big pot to put the wisdom in. Where, oh where, could he get the perfect pot, Anansi wondered. And as he was wondering, his eye chanced to look across the stream, toward the workplace of his son Kweku, the potmaker.

Kweku was sitting in the yard in front of his hut, completely absorbed in putting flower heads in a small gourd, adding water, and grinding the mixture to a soft paste,

which he then rubbed on the pots. Each color was made from a different flower, which had to be collected early in the morning while the dew was still on it. As he ground and painted, Kweku hummed happily to himself. He liked what he was doing, and he tried very hard to do it well. The years of care and practice were worth it, he thought, and apparently others agreed. At the last Trading Day, he had heard someone talking about how fine his lines were and how bright his colors. His thoughts must have distracted him, though, for as he put the finishing touches on the new gourd for old Keetu, his hand slipped a bit and the red dye ran ever so slightly into the blue. Old Keetu wouldn't notice, her eyes were not very good; nevertheless, he put that pot aside for his own use and started all over again.

He was concentrating so hard on getting the new gourd ready in time that he didn't notice his visitor until it was almost too late. Meru, the monkey, had run into the yard, bent on mischief, rolling the small gourds like balls, knocking over the large gourds, and getting into everything.

''What do you want, little one?'' said Kweku.

Meru made a rude noise and raced around the yard even faster, knocking over more pots.

How can I stop him? thought Kweku. Words are no good, and I am too slow to catch him before real damage is done. Just as the monkey started to run off with a large pot almost too big for him to handle, Kweku realized what he must do.

He reached over to a nearby tree, plucked a piece of ripe fruit, held it up, and sniffed it. Then he took a large, noisy bite out of the fruit. Meru smelled the fruit and turned around. Kweku walked toward his hut, stumbled over a pebble, and let the fruit fly from his hand. Meru let go of the large pot, raced across the yard, snatched up the fruit, and ran off with it.

Kweku smiled, happy that he had remembered the saying that his mother had taught him — a thief enjoys stealing.

No sooner was he back at work, then in walked his father, muttering to himself, and looking very irritated.

''What's the matter, Father?'' asked Kweku.

''I wanted one of your large pots.''

''Well, you shall have one.''

''No,'' said Anansi. ''I didn't want to bother you, so I sent Meru to get one for me, but he hasn't returned.

I suppose he ran off with it himself. Although what a monkey would do with a large pot is more than I can understand.''

Kweku smiled more to himself than to his father. So the Spider was up to his old tricks, and now he was blaming the monkey for not doing a wicked deed. Anansi didn't even seem to realize that what he had planned was wrong. Whatever was in the Spider's house belonged to the spider; whatever was outside the Spider's house belonged to him too.

''Well, Father. I'm sorry you had such trouble. Why don't you pick a pot and take it home with you. Consider it a gift from me.''

Anansi looked around, but there was no pot big enough. ''I'm afraid you don't have any big pots.''

''I have nothing bigger than these . . .''

''Oh, yes, you do. Don't try to hide it from me. It's right over there,'' Anansi pointed to the largest gourd he had ever seen. It was right outside the door of Kweku's hut.

''That is my water barrel, Father. But if you want it, you can have it.''

Anansi smiled, happy at last, went to the water barrel and upended it, wasting all the water that Kweku had collected. Then, huffing and puffing, he walked off with the huge pot, without even a thank-you to his son.

That night, still in his man shape, he tiptoed out of his hut well after midnight. When he reached his neighbor's hut, he put the large pot down, took two deep breaths, and changed into a tiny spider. In a few minutes, he had crawled to the bedroll; a few seconds more, he had reached the man's ear. Reaching inside the ear with his delicate front legs, he stole the man's wisdom, wrapped it in spider silk, and carried it out to the pot. Then he changed into the man shape again, put the wisdom into the pot, and went on to the next hut. From village to village and from animal den to animal den he went, collecting wisdom all through the night.

One hour before dawn, his pot was full.

''Now I must hide it.''

First he sealed up the pot so tightly that not even the smallest ant could get in. Then he carried it deep into the forest until he came to the highest tree. So far into the forest was he that the new light had not yet touched the forest floor. Anansi looked up at the very large tree, then down at the very large pot, and said, ''I have been busy all night. I think I will rest my eyes, just for a bit.'' And in less than a minute, he was asleep.

While he slept, the rays of light began to touch the forest floor, picking out the figure of a man. It was Kweku, gathering leaves and flowers to make paints for his pots. As he plucked each one, he called it by its name, and thanked it for giving him its beauty. Then he wrapped it in a leaf and put it in the gourd that he had slung over his back.

Kweku was within yards of the big tree before he saw Anansi Spider and the big pot. He stopped and watched, sure that his father was up to no good.

Anansi, feeling the sun on him, stretched, yawned and swung the huge pot in front of him, hanging it from a cord tied round his neck. Then he began to climb. But every time he tried to pull his legs up, the pot came between him and the tree. Again and again he tried, and again and again he failed.

Kweku could contain himself no longer. ''Father!''

Anansi jumped so high he almost made it up the first twenty feet of the tree, but the huge pot got in the way again.

''Kweku, what are you doing here?''

''I was collecting my flowers, and then I saw you. What are you doing here?''

''Isn't it obvious? I'm trying to climb a tree!''

Kweku chuckled. His father frowned. ''Why are you laughing?''

''Because you're so funny, Father. You're usually so clever. I wonder why you haven't thought to let the pot hang down your back?''

And he laughed again.

At that Anansi Spider lost his temper. Of course, Kweku was right. That was the best way to handle the problem. It was the wise thing to do. Then what, he asked himself, was the use of a pot of wisdom if it didn't tell him how to climb a tree?

He got so mad that he began to breathe harder and harder and deeper and deeper. He breathed so hard that he began to lose his human shape and shrink into his spider form. Now, the smaller he got, the looser grew the cord around his neck. Finally the cord slipped off, sending the pot crashing to the ground, where it smashed into a thousand pieces.

And all the wisdom of the world, which Anansi Spider had worked so hard to gather, became a thousand sparks of light, flying every which way, back to the animals and people from whom he had taken it.

How to Become a Smart Shopper

Smart shoppers know how to shop. They know what is worth buying and what isn't. They look for ways to save, and — even more important — they know how to recognize bargains that aren't really money-savers.

A Guide to Stores

If you want to be a smart shopper, the first thing to learn is *where* to shop. Look around your neighborhood. You will probably notice a number of different kinds of stores. *Large supermarkets* carry many different kinds of food in many brands and sizes. Their prices are usually lower than at other types of stores, and some supermarkets will deliver your groceries, for a small charge.

Small neighborhood grocery stores do not carry as many brands or sizes or types of food as supermarkets do, and their prices are usually higher. Small neighborhood stores often give better service, though. They may deliver — either for free or for a small charge. And some will take orders on the phone or let you buy on credit. There are times when these conveniences might be important to you.

Some stores are *specialty stores.* They carry only one kind of food — for example, meat or fish or baked goods or dairy products or fruits and vegetables. The quality is often higher in these stores than in supermarkets. You may find special cuts or varieties or brands that are not available in the supermarket, and the service may be better. But the prices are also higher.

In farming country, you can often find *roadside stands* that sell fresh fruits and vegetables. The quality is usually excellent — the fruits and vegetables may have been picked only a few hours before — and the prices are often quite low. Unless you live in the country, these stands may be hard to get to, and they don't deliver to your home. They can be worth a trip if you can buy in quantity and preserve or freeze some of your purchases.

Choosing a Supermarket

Even if you have decided to save money by shopping at a supermarket, you may have a choice of supermarkets in your neighborhood. Food prices can vary from one market to another. The supermarket nearest you may charge more for almost every item than the store a few blocks farther away.

To find the store with the best prices, price a sampling of items like the one below:

> ground beef — 1 pound
> chicken — 1 pound
> fresh whole milk — 1 quart
> grade A medium eggs — 1 dozen
> bananas — 1 pound
> frozen orange juice — small (6 ounce) can
> canned peas — 1 pound (16 ounces)
> sliced bread — 1 pound loaf

Take this list to each store that is within walking distance from where you live, or within a few minutes by car if you use the car to shop. Price each item in the amount listed. Write down the price for the *least expensive* brand in each case. Then add up all the prices to see which store charges the least.

Deciding What to Buy

Once you're inside the store, you still have decisions to make. Here are some guidelines to help you.

1. When you are buying packaged foods of any kind, look at how much the package weighs or how much it holds. One package may be stamped $1.60 and the other $2.40. But if the second package holds twice as much as the first one, then it is a better buy.

2. Whenever possible, check the unit prices. These are special labels that show not only what the whole item costs but what the price per pound is. For example, a chicken might cost $3.83 but have a unit price of 89 cents a pound. It's the price per pound (or per pint or quart) that you use to compare the cost of one item with another.

3. Fresh fruits, vegetables, meats, and milk are often better for you (and sometimes cheaper) than canned or frozen or dried ones, but they are not necessarily a better buy. Fresh foods usually spoil easily. It isn't wise to buy them in large quantity unless you can freeze them. It's hard for one or two people to eat a whole cabbage or a whole melon before it spoils. Even though the per-pound price on an item like this might be low, if you end up paying for three pounds and only eating half of it, it is not a bargain. When you shop for fresh foods, think about how much of it you will use right away. Think about how much preparation and clean-up time is needed for fresh foods. Then think about whether using frozen, canned, or packaged items makes more sense in some cases.

Saving on Food Prices

There are a number of ways to save money on food, in addition to checking the unit price to find out which item is the best buy.

1. Look for the *house* brand. Many large supermar-

ket chains have their own brand of canned or frozen foods and household products. These are called house brands. They are usually just as good as nationally advertised products and are sometimes cheaper. Ask the store manager for the house brand names — they are often not the same as the name of the store. Remember to compare prices, though. Just because a product is a house brand doesn't guarantee that it will be your best buy.

2. Look for items that are *on sale*. Most supermarkets have special weekly sales on different items and brands. Ask the store manager about these sales, or look for the store's newspaper ads. Remember, though, to check the unit price and compare prices, even on sale items. Even if one brand is on sale, another brand may be still cheaper. Make sure, too, that the food is fresh. Packaged foods are stamped with dates that tell you how long the contents will remain fresh. Out-of-date items are not always removed from the shelves. When you do see a good bargain, stock up for the weeks ahead. Just make sure you have enough storage space for what you buy. If you have freezer space, sale time is a good time to stock up on expensive items such as meat.

3. Use *coupons* whenever it makes sense to. Coupons — which may be printed in newspapers or magazines, mailed to your house, or packaged with a product — offer discounts on certain products. Some stores run special double coupon sales. Your coupons will give you double the discount then. You must use coupons carefully for them to save you money. Check the expiration date; the coupon cannot be used after that date. Look for special conditions. Some coupons are good only in certain stores. Others say you have to buy a certain size of the product (usually a large size) to get the discount. And some say you have to buy more than one of the product. Make sure the coupons really save you money. Even with a coupon discount, a product may still cost more than another brand you might buy instead.

4. Take advantage of *refund offers*. Some companies offer refunds to get people to try their products. The refund may be for a set amount or for the entire purchase price of an item. To get the refund, you must send the manufacturer the special refund form and, usually, some *proof of purchase*, such as a seal or label from the package. Sometimes a company will ask for the sales slip or register receipt too. Most refund offers have an expiration date and require 2-5 proofs of purchase (which means buying the product 2-5 times). Also, most refunds are only given one to a family and may take 4-8 weeks to arrive. So, refunds may only be worthwhile if you buy the product regularly and remember to save the proofs of purchase.

A Mother in Mannville

by Marjorie Kinnan Rawlings

The orphanage is high in the Carolina mountains. Sometimes in winter the snowdrifts are so deep that the institution is cut off from the village below, from all the world. Fog hides the mountain peaks, the snow swirls down the valleys, and a wind blows so bitterly that the orphanage boys who take the milk twice daily to the baby cottage reach the door with fingers stiff in an agony of numbness.

"Or when we carry trays from the cookhouse for the ones that are sick," Jerry said, "we get our faces frostbit, because we can't put our hands over them. I have gloves," he added. "Some of the boys don't have any."

He liked the late spring, he said. The rhododendron was in bloom, a carpet of color, across the mountainsides, soft as the May winds that stirred the hemlocks. He called it laurel.

"It's pretty when the laurel blooms," he said. "Some of it's pink and some of it's white."

I was there in the autumn. I wanted quiet, isolation, to do some troublesome writing. I wanted mountain air to blow out the malaria from too long a time in the subtropics. I was homesick, too, for the flaming of maples in October, and for corn shocks and pumpkins and black-walnut trees and the lift of hills. I found them all, living in a cabin that belonged to the orphanage, half a mile beyond the orphanage farm. When I took the cabin, I asked for a boy or a man to come and chop wood for the fireplace. The first few days were warm, I found what wood I needed about the cabin, no one came, and I forgot the order.

I looked up from my typewriter one late afternoon, a little startled. A boy stood at the door, and my pointer dog, my companion, was at his side and had not barked to warn me. The boy was probably twelve years old, but undersized. He wore overalls and a torn shirt, and was barefooted.

He said, "I can chop some wood today."

I said, "But I have a boy coming from the orphanage."

"I'm the boy."

"You? But you're small."

"Size don't matter, chopping wood," he said. "Some of the big boys don't chop good. I've been chopping wood at the orphanage a long time."

I visualized mangled and inadequate branches for my fires. I was well into my work and not inclined to conversation. I was a little blunt.

"Very well. There's the ax. Go ahead and see what you can do."

I went back to work, closing the door. At first the sound of the boy dragging brush annoyed me. Then he began to chop. The blows were rhythmic and steady, and shortly I had forgotten him, the sound no more of an interruption than a consistent rain. I suppose an hour and a half passed, for when I stopped and stretched, and heard the boy's steps on the cabin stoop, the sun was dropping behind the farthest mountain, and the valleys were purple with something deeper than the asters.

The boy said, "I have to go to supper now. I can come again tomorrow evening."

I said, "I'll pay you now for what you've done," thinking I should probably have to insist on an older boy. "Ten cents an hour?"

"Anything is all right."

We went together back of the cabin. An astonishing amount of solid wood had been cut. There were cherry logs and heavy roots of rhododendron, and blocks from the waste pine and oak left from the building of the cabin.

"But you've done as much as a man," I said. "This is a splendid pile."

I looked at him, actually, for the first time. His hair was the color of the corn shocks and his eyes, very direct, were like the mountain sky when rain is pending — gray, with a shadowing of that miraculous blue. As I spoke, a light came over him, as though the setting of the sun had touched him with the same suffused glory with which it touched the mountains. I gave him a quarter.

"You may come tomorrow," I said, "and thank you very much."

He looked at me, and at the coin, and seemed to want to speak, but could not, and turned away.

"I'll split kindling tomorrow," he said over his thin, ragged shoulder. "You'll need kindling and medium wood and logs and backlogs."

At daylight I was half wakened by the sound of chopping. Again it was so even in texture that I went back to sleep. When I left my bed in the cool morning, the boy had come and gone, and a stack of kindling was neat against the cabin wall. He came again after school in the afternoon and worked until time to return to the orphanage. His name was Jerry; he was twelve years old, and he had been at the orphanage since he was four. I could picture him at four, with the same grave gray-blue eyes and the same — independence? No, the word that comes to me is "integrity."

The word means something very special to me, and the quality for which I use it is a rare one. My father had it — there is another of whom I am almost sure — but almost no man of my acquaintance possesses it with the clarity, the purity, the simplicity of a mountain stream. But the boy Jerry had it. It is bedded on courage, but it is more than brave. It is honest, but it is more than honesty. The ax handle broke one day. Jerry said the woodshop at the orphanage would repair it. I brought money to pay for the job, and he refused it.

"I'll pay for it," he said. "I broke it. I brought the ax down careless."

"But no one hits accurately every time," I told him. "The fault was in the wood of the handle. I'll see the man from whom I bought it."

It was only then that he would take the money. He was standing back of his own carelessness. He was a free-will agent, and he chose to do careful work; and if he failed, he took the responsibility without subterfuge.

And he did for me the unnecessary thing, the gracious thing, that we find done only by the great of heart. Things no training can teach, for they are done on the instant, with no predicated experience. He found a cubbyhole beside the fireplace that I had not noticed. There, of his own accord, he put kindling and "medium" wood, so that I might always have dry fire material ready in case of sudden wet weather. A stone was loose in the rough walk to the cabin. He dug a deeper hole and steadied it, although he came, himself, by a short cut over the bank. I found that when I tried to return his thoughtfulness with such things as candy and apples, he was wordless. "Thank you" was, perhaps, an expression for which he had had no use, for his courtesy was instinctive. He only looked at the gift and at me, and a curtain lifted, so that I saw deep into the clear well of his eyes, and gratitude was there, and affection, soft over the firm granite of his character.

He made simple excuses to come and sit with me. I could no more have turned him away than if he had been physically hungry. I suggested once that the best time for us to visit was just before supper, when I left off my writing. After that, he waited always until my typewriter had been some time quiet. One day I worked until nearly dark. I went outside the cabin, having forgotten him. I saw him going up over the hill in the twilight toward the orphanage. When I sat down on my stoop, a place was warm from his body where he had been sitting.

He became intimate, of course, with my pointer, Pat. There is a strange communion between a boy and a dog. Perhaps they possess the same singleness of spirit, the same kind of wisdom. It is difficult to explain, but it exists. When I went across the state for a weekend, I left the dog in Jer-

ry's charge. I gave him the dog whistle and the key to the cabin, and left sufficient food. He was to come two or three times a day and let out the dog, and feed and exercise him. I should return Sunday night, and Jerry would take out the dog for the last time Sunday afternoon and then leave the key under an agreed hiding place.

My return was belated, and fog filled the mountain passes so treacherously that I dared not drive at night. The fog held the next morning, and it was Monday noon before I reached the cabin. The dog had been fed and cared for that morning. Jerry came early in the afternoon, anxious.

"The superintendent said nobody would drive in the fog," he said. "I came just before bedtime last night and you hadn't come. So I brought Pat some of my breakfast this morning. I wouldn't have let anything happen to him."

"I was sure of that. I didn't worry."

"When I heard about the fog, I thought you'd know."

He was needed for work at the orphanage, and he had to return at once. I gave him a dollar in payment, and he looked at it and went away. But that night he came in the darkness and knocked at the door.

"Come in, Jerry," I said, "if you're allowed to be away this late."

"I told maybe a story," he said. "I told them I thought you would want to see me."

"That's true," I assured him, and I saw his relief. "I want to hear about how you managed with the dog."

He sat by the fire with me, with no other light, and told me of their two days together. The dog lay close to him, and found a comfort there that I did not have for him. And it seemed to me that being with my dog, and caring for him, had brought the boy and me, too, together, so that he felt that he belonged to me as well as to the animal.

"He stayed right with me," he told me, "except when he ran in the laurel. He likes the laurel. I took him up over the hill and we both ran fast. There was a place where the grass was high and I lay down in it and hid. I could hear Pat hunting for me. He found my trail and he barked. When he found me, he acted crazy, and he ran around and around me, in circles."

We watched the flames.

"That's an apple log," he said. "It burns the prettiest of any wood."

We were very close.

He was suddenly impelled to speak of things he had not spoken of before, nor had I cared to ask him.

"You look a little bit like my mother," he said. "Especially in the dark, by the fire."

"But you were only four, Jerry, when you came here. You have remembered how she looked, all these years?"

"My mother lives in Mannville," he said.

For a moment, finding that he had a mother shocked

me as greatly as anything in my life has ever done, and I did not know why it disturbed me. Then I understood my distress. I was filled with a passionate resentment that any woman should go away and leave her son. A fresh anger added itself. A son like this one — The orphanage was a wholesome place, the executives were kind, good people, the food was more than adequate, the boys were healthy, a ragged shirt was no hardship, nor the doing of clean labor. Granted, perhaps, that the boy felt no lack, what blood fed the bowels of a woman who did not yearn over this child's lean body that had come in parturition out of her own? At four he would have looked the same as now. Nothing, I thought, nothing in life could change those eyes. His quality must be apparent to an idiot, a fool. I burned with questions I could not ask. In any case, I was afraid, there would be pain.

"Have you seen her, Jerry — lately?"

"I see her every summer. She sends for me."

I wanted to cry out, "Why are you not with her? How can she let you go away again?"

He said, "She comes up here from Mannville whenever she can. She doesn't have a job now."

His face shone in the firelight.

"She wanted to give me a puppy, but they can't let any one boy keep a puppy. You remember the suit I had on last Sunday?" He was plainly proud. "She sent me that for Christmas. The Christmas before that" — he drew a long breath, savoring the memory — "she sent me a pair of skates."

"Roller skates?"

My mind was busy, making pictures of her, trying to understand her. She had not, then, entirely deserted or forgotten him. But why, then — I thought, "I must not condemn her without knowing."

"Roller skates. I let the other boys use them. They're always borrowing them. But they're careful of them."

What circumstance other than poverty —

"I'm going to take the dollar you gave me for taking care of Pat," he said, "and buy her a pair of gloves."

I could only say, "That will be nice. Do you know her size?"

"I think it's 8½," he said.

He looked at my hands.

"Do you wear 8½?" he asked.

"No. I wear a smaller size, a 6."

"Oh! Then I guess her hands are bigger than yours."

I hated her. Poverty or no, there was other food than bread, and the soul could starve as quickly as the body. He was taking his dollar to buy gloves for her big stupid hands, and she lived away from him, in Mannville, and contented herself with sending him skates.

"She likes white gloves," he said. "Do you think I can get them for a dollar?"

"I think so," I said.

I decided that I should not leave the mountains without seeing her and knowing for myself why she had done this thing.

The human mind scatters its interests as though made of thistledown, and every wind stirs and moves it. I finished my work. It did not please me, and I gave my thoughts to another field. I should need some Mexican material.

I made arrangements to close my Florida place. Mexico immediately, and doing the writing there, if conditions were favorable. Then, Alaska with my brother. After that, heaven knew what or where.

I did not take time to go to Mannville to see Jerry's mother, nor even to talk with the orphanage officials about her. I was a trifle abstracted about the boy, because of my work and plans. And after my first fury at her — we did not speak of her again — his having a mother, any sort at all, not far away, in Mannville, relieved me of the ache I had had about him. He did not question the anomalous relation. He was not lonely. It was none of my concern.

He came every day and cut my wood and did small helpful favors and stayed to talk. The days had become cold, and often I let him come inside the cabin. He would lie on the floor in front of the fire, with one arm across the pointer, and they would both doze and wait quietly for me. Other days they ran with a common ecstasy through the laurel, and since the asters were now gone, he brought me back vermilion maple leaves, and chestnut boughs dripping with imperial yellow. I was ready to go.

I said to him, "You have been my good friend, Jerry. I shall often think of you and miss you. Pat will miss you too. I am leaving tomorrow."

He did not answer. When he went away, I remember that a new moon hung over the mountains, and I watched him go in silence up the hill. I expected him the next day, but he did not come. The details of packing my personal belongings, loading my car, arranging the bed over the seat, where the dog would ride, occupied me until late in the day. I closed the cabin and started the car, noticing that the sun was in the west and I should do well to be out of the mountains by nightfall. I stopped by the orphanage and left the cabin key and money for my light bill with Miss Clark.

"And will you call Jerry for me to say goodbye to him?"

"I don't know where he is," she said. "I'm afraid he's not well. He didn't eat his dinner this noon. One of the other boys saw him going over the hill into the laurel. He was supposed to fire the boiler this afternoon. It's not like him; he's unusually reliable."

I was almost relieved, for I knew I should never see him again, and it would be easier not to say goodbye to him.

I said, "I wanted to talk with you about his mother — why he's here — but I'm in more of a hurry than I expected to be. It's out of the question for me to see her now. But here's some money I'd like to leave with you to buy things for him at Christmas and on his birthday. It will be better than for me to try to send him things. I could so easily duplicate — skates, for instance."

She blinked her eyes.

"There's not much use for skates here," she said. Her stupidity annoyed me.

"What I mean," I said, "is that I don't want to duplicate things his mother sends him. I might have chosen skates if I didn't know she had already given them to him."

She stared at me.

"I don't understand," she said. "He has no mother. He has no skates."

The Virginia Colony
by Hilarie Staton

The London Company

About 20 years after the mysterious disappearance of the English colony on Roanoke Island, the English decided to start more colonies in North America. The London Company was formed to start one in Virginia. It was a "joint-stock" company, which meant people bought shares, or pieces, of the company. The money paid for the shares was used to start and run the colony. When the company made money, it would be split between the people who owned shares. Many people bought shares in the London Company.

The London Company got its charter, or written permission, from the king. The colony was run by the company's directors in England, who made all the important decisions. The colonists worked for the company, which owned all the land.

The Early Days

The first colonists arrived in 1607. They named their town Jamestown for King James. It seemed like a good place, but the swamp nearby was unhealthy. Over the years, thousands of colonists died there.

The first colonists wanted to look for gold, not build houses or plant corn. Over half of them died that first winter. They weren't trained to survive in the woods, to farm, or even to build a house. One man, Captain John Smith, forced them to do these life-saving jobs, but the colonists did not like him. When he left, no other leader made Jamestown's colonists work for the good of all.

For many years the town stayed small. The colonists had to learn ways of the past, like clearing trees and protecting themselves from attack. Tools such as the gun and the ax became important to their survival. The colonists waited for food from England rather than hunting or growing their own food. If they were starving, they raided Indian villages. Their few cows and pigs ran loose in the woods and destroyed the Indians' cornfields.

The London Company was not happy with their colony. No gold was found. Many colonists died, and the rest were mistreating the Indians. The company made some changes. For each person who came to Jamestown, land was given to the person who paid their fare. The bigger the group, the more land they got. Now, many farmers came to Virginia to start their own farms. Those who could brought many people so they could get more land.

The company, however, continued to control trade. They demanded that farmers grow what people in England wanted. They told the farmers to grow silk, sugar, and hemp for rope — none of which would grow in Virginia. Quickly, the company found that it couldn't enforce these rules from across the ocean.

Tobacco Arrives.

In 1612, John Rolfe made a discovery that changed Jamestown. He discovered that West Indian tobacco grew well in Virginia, and it sold for high prices in England. Soon everyone in Virginia was growing it. Some even grew tobacco instead of food.

The unexpected problem was that tobacco used up the soil after a few years, and fresh land was always needed. That didn't bother the colonists; there was plenty of rich land. The colonists believed that the land belonged to the King, not to the Indians. Besides, the colonists thought, Indians move around a lot. Let them move somewhere else. So the tobacco farmers cleared the forests which housed the animals the Indians hunted. The animals left, and there was less food for both the Indians and the colonists.

Scarce Labor

Growing tobacco was hard work, and each farmer wanted to grow as much tobacco as he could. There was plenty of land, but not enough workers. The rich were those farmers that had the most workers. The colonists solved this problem in several ways.

Many colonists paid for workers to come from England. These workers were called "indentured servants." These people were too poor to pay their own way. A colonist paid their transportation and then housed and fed them for about five years. In return, the servants worked without pay until their time was up. Then they were given some tools, clothes, and maybe land. Then they were on their own. Some servants continued to work for the same people, but for pay. Most started their own farms.

At first, few women came to Jamestown, but as farms spread along the rivers, more and more women came to Virginia. They married and raised large families, partly to have more help around the farm. The whole family worked long hours.

Another kind of worker was used after 1619, when a Dutch ship brought some African blacks to Jamestown. No one is sure if these people were sold as slaves or as indentured servants. A few of those early blacks became free farmers. But the blacks who arrived later were held as slaves. They had no real chance to become free.

Another way the colonists solved the worker shortage was by learning to do many things for themselves. In England, landowners hired someone to do a job and bought products already made by trained craftsmen. In Virginia, colonists were forced to be independent. Few people were trained for special jobs, like doctor or weaver. Colonists soon discovered they had to be farmer, doctor, teacher, blacksmith, weaver, and candlemaker. They had to learn many different tasks.

Representative Government.

About the time Rolfe brought tobacco to Virginia, the colonial government was changed. The London Company still appointed the governor, usually from England, but a group of important Virginians now helped make the decisions.

In England, many people had a say in their government and the colonists wanted a voice in Virginia's government, too. The London Company set up the House of Burgesses. It was the first representative assembly in the New World.

Virginians elected representatives to the House of Burgesses. At first, most white men could vote. Later, only those who owned a certain amount of property could vote. No women or blacks could vote. All the laws had to be approved by the company directors in London.

The Virginians worked hard in the House of Burgesses. They wrote laws and collected taxes. Many of their laws were different from English laws, because they were meeting new situations. No one in England had to protect farms, build roads through the wilderness, or decide borders. The colonists did.

Changes

As time went by, new colonists came. Many were unprepared for the hardships they found on Virginian farms, yet few settled in towns. Jamestown was still an unhealthy place. It wasn't until 1691 that the Virginians finally moved their capital away from the swamp to Williamsburg.

Since there were no deep harbors in Virginia, no trading seaport city was built. Farms were cleared along the rivers. These rivers were deep enough to allow ships to travel up them. They became the colony's highways. Ships came right to the farm. Goods ordered from England were delivered and tobacco was loaded directly onto the ships.

At first, most farm families had a small home and a vegetable garden. Many farms had two or three indentured servants who helped with the field work and the house work. Later, larger farms, called plantations, developed. They had many workers, most of them slaves. Each large farm was like a miniature village. A school, church, store, and blacksmith shop were all right on a plantation.

More and more colonists came. Some came as indentured servants, others as freemen. The best land along the rivers was quickly taken. Later colonists had to move inland and west to find open land, as did indentured servants when they became free. These small farmers had little representation in the House of Burgesses. They didn't have rivers for transportation, so it took a long time for news or goods to reach them. The Indians, whose land they took, attacked them and burned their houses and fields.

In 1675, the House of Burgesses voted to build forts in the east to protect the large, rich farms. The small western farmers were very upset. They were being attacked more often than the eastern farmers, but they had no protection. They organized under a young planter named Nathaniel Bacon. They destroyed a peaceful Indian tribe and then marched to Jamestown. They told the governor and the House of Burgesses that they wanted representation and protection. Although some of their demands were met, many of the leaders were killed for their part in "Bacon's Rebellion."

At first, the English did not find what they wanted in Virginia. Over the years, the colonists forgot hunting for gold and became tobacco farmers. They made many changes in their lives to fit the place they lived. They developed a government, culture and technology to make their colony work.

The Massachusetts Colonies

by Hilarie Staton

New England was settled by a different type of person than came to Jamestown. New England colonists came to America for different reasons. They thought different things were important. They had to adjust to a different environment, and so a different way of life developed.

The Plymouth Colony

Puritans and Separatists. In the years before the first English colonies were started, religion in England had changed. The country's official religion had been Roman Catholic until King Henry VIII left that church. He created a new one, the Church of England.

As the years went by, different groups formed within the Church of England. Some people wanted the church to change many things. They wanted to make the church "pure" again, and so were called "Puritans." Other people thought that too many changes were needed, and that the Church of England would never be the way they wanted it. They wanted to be separate from it, so they were called "Separatists."

One group of Separatists was not treated well in England because of their beliefs, so they moved to Holland. After a while, they decided that they did not want to become Dutch. England was their country, but they were not happy there.

The Plymouth Company. At the same time that the London Company received its charter, the Plymouth Company got one, too. This joint-stock company was to build a colony in the northern part of Virginia. The company offered the Separatists in Holland a chance to move to America. The company would pay their way, if they would work for the company. The Separatists agreed.

They left England in the ship *Mayflower* in 1620. After many storms, they finally landed at Plymouth Rock near Cape Cod, Massachusetts. They decided this was a good place to settle, so they stayed. They are known in American history as the Pilgrims.

Since they were not in Virginia, some of the Pilgrims felt the Plymouth Company was not responsible for them. They wrote a "compact." In this Mayflower Compact, they agreed that they would help each other. They would govern themselves and work together for the good of their community.

Since they landed just before winter, they weren't pre-pared for the harsh winds, deep snow, and biting cold of a New England winter. Half of the Pilgrims died before spring. When spring came, the local Indians helped those left. With their help, the Pilgrims took in a large harvest that fall. To thank the Indians, the Pilgrims invited them to a Thanksgiving feast. The feast, though enjoyed by all, used many of the Pilgrim's winter supplies. They learned that they would have to be more careful with their food.

The Massachusetts Bay Colony

A Special Place. In 1629, the Massachusetts Bay Company was founded by a group of English Puritans. This joint-stock company sold its shares only to other Puritans. The share holders were to be the colonists, too. When the Puritan colonists left for Massachusetts, they took the company's charter with them. Unlike other company colonies, their directors were in the colony. They knew at first hand the problems of the colony. These colonists governed themselves.

The Puritans wanted to create what they felt was a perfect place using English laws, hard work, and their religion. They wanted their example to change the way people in England thought about life and religion.

The Puritans were not just religious, but practical, too. Many Puritans had successful businesses in England. They knew they could not make it alone, so they brought farmers, blacksmiths and other craftsmen with them. This was the largest group of colonists (900-1,000) to leave England together.

The Puritans felt religion and government should be combined. Their laws did just that. By law, everyone had to attend a Puritan church. Only certain Puritans, called Church Members, could vote. The Church Members elected an assembly and a governor. Many people who disagreed with these laws left or were made to leave the colony. Some began new colonies farther west, in what is now Rhode Island and Connecticut.

Towns from the Beginning. The Massachusetts Bay Company gave land to a whole town, not to one family. Boston and several nearby towns were the first. Each town shared the best land and divided up the rest for homes, a church, a school, and fields. Since church attendance was required, people lived in town, where the church was. Houses were built around a town square. Schools were started and all children attended. Storekeepers and craftsmen quickly set up shop. A town meeting, open to all land-owning men, decided important matters, such as roads, schools and timber cutting.

Many new settlers came to Massachusetts. If they wanted to move into an older community, they had to be accepted by everyone who lived there. Other colonists joined together, got a grant from the Company, and built towns to the west. Soon there were many small towns in the colony.

The environment that the Massachusetts settlers found was very different from Virginia. There were no rivers for transportation, so roads were built. Travel between towns was slow and rough. Farmers worked hard to clear the thick forests and rocky soil. Some timber was sent to England, especially long straight trunks which were used to build ships. The soil was not rich, but enough was grown to feed the family. Most farmers did not grow enough to ship crops to other places.

Trade. All over New England, the colonists learned to adapt to the hard winters. They made use of the long days in front of the fire. Each family made things, like but-tons, brooms, or nails. As a family made more than they could use, they traded with their neighbors for what they made. Then, after they had traded with everyone in town, they went to other towns. These family businesses became important to New England.

When there were extra products that no one in New England wanted, merchants took them to other parts of the world. Soon New England timber was used to build ships right in the colonies. Captains took the products along with timber, fish, furs, and livestock to other colonies, to England, Africa, and to the West Indies.

Some ships went directly to one place and returned. Other ships followed the "triangle trade." Ships from New England went to the West Indies with food and livestock. Then molasses and sugar from there were taken to England. From England, the ships returned to the colonies with European products. Other ships brought black Africans to the West Indies or southern colonies, where they were sold as slaves. Then they loaded sugar or tobacco and returned to New England. All this trade made New England merchants and shipbuilders rich.

The Respiratory System

All animals have some method of taking oxygen in from the environment and returning carbon dioxide to the environment. This process of exchange is known as *respiration*. Very simple forms of animal life exchange oxygen and carbon dioxide by the form of respiration known as *diffusion*. Diffusion is the movement of a substance from an area where a great deal of it occurs to an area where there is less of it. If there is a higher concentration of oxygen in the outside environment than in the animal, the oxygen will move by diffusion through the animal's skin and into its cells. In the same way, the carbon dioxide within the animal will move out into the environment.

More complex animals cannot survive by diffusion. They need a more complex system of respiration. Land animals most commonly have *lungs* to aid them in the exchange of oxygen and carbon dioxide.

Let us look at how the human respiratory system works. When we breathe, we contract the chest muscle known as the *diaphragm*, which causes the air pressure in the lungs to drop and the chest cavity to expand. In response to that drop in pressure, air moves in from the outside.

We take in this air through the nose, where it is warmed up before moving farther into the body. The nose also filters dust out of the air. The air then travels to the *pharynx*, at the back of the throat, through the *glottis*, and into the *larynx*, or voice box. Next the air passes through the *trachea*, or *windpipe*, where it is once more cleaned. Mucus and dirt are swept out by *cilia*, which are structures like little hairs, and pushed back up toward the pharynx. At its lower end, the trachea forms two branches, or *bronchi*, one leading into each lung. Within the lungs, the bronchi branch even more, forming *bronchioles*. The bronchioles end in groups of tiny sacs called *alveoli*.

The alveoli are the sites of the carbon dioxide-oxygen exchange. They are covered by a thin membrane that both oxygen and carbon dioxide can cross. The walls of the alveoli are also full of the tiny blood vessels called *capillaries*, and the blood in these capillaries contains less oxygen than the air we take into our lungs. Therefore, the oxygen in the alveoli moves into the blood, and the carbon dioxide in the blood moves into the alveoli.

From the alveoli, the air containing the carbon dioxide passes in reverse along the same path that it came in. It goes from the bronchioles to the bronchi and then through the trachea. Next, the carbon dioxide-laden air passes into the larynx, through the glottis, and then to the pharynx, before being exhaled through the nose.

The Circulatory System

The circulatory system is controlled by the heart, which is made up of two pumps — one on the left side of the heart and one on the right side. Each side has two chambers. The upper chamber is called the *atrium,* and the lower is the *ventricle.* The upper and lower chambers on each side are connected by a valve that directs the flow of the blood.

The job of the right side of the heart is to receive blood returning from the body. This blood is high in carbon dioxide, and must be sent to the lungs to exchange the carbon dioxide for oxygen. This blood enters the right side of the heart through two large veins known as the *venae cavae* and empties into the right atrium. When the atrium is full, it contracts and forces the blood through the valve into the right ventricle. Then the right ventricle contracts and forces the blood past another valve and into the *pulmonary artery.* The pulmonary artery carries the blood into the capillaries of the lungs.

When the carbon dioxide in the capillaries has been exchanged for oxygen, the blood moves into the *pulmonary veins,* which carry it back to the heart. The oxygenated blood passes into the heart's left atrium. When this atrium is full, it contracts and sends the blood into the left ventricle. From the left ventricle the oxygenated blood is forced by another contraction into the *aorta.* This is a huge artery with branches leading to all parts of the body. Once the blood has supplied the body with oxygen, it returns to the heart through the veins, carrying carbon dioxide back to the right atrium. Now the whole process is ready to begin again.

The Sniper

by Liam O'Flaherty

[This story takes place in the city of Dublin, the capital of Ireland, sometime in the early 1920's. At that time, Ireland had won a measure of independence from Britain, only to plunge into a civil war over just how much independence Ireland was to have. The "Free Staters" formed the government in power. They were willing to settle for what Britain offered: a self-governing "Free State" within the British Commonwealth for all but 6 of Ireland's 32 counties. Opposing them were the "Republicans," who demanded more: total independence from Britain and a union of all 32 counties in an Irish Republic.

The action of the story takes place near the O'Connell Bridge over the River Liffey, which flows through the center of Dublin.]

The long June twilight faded into night. Dublin lay enveloped in darkness but for the dim light of the moon that shone through fleecy clouds, casting a pale light as of approaching dawn over the streets and the dark waters of the Liffey. Around the beleaguered Four Courts the heavy guns roared. Here and there through the city, machine-guns and rifles broke the silence of the night, spasmodically, like dogs barking on lone farms. Republicans and Free Staters were waging civil war.

On a roof-top near O'Connell Bridge, a Republican sniper lay watching. Beside him lay his rifle and over his shoulders were slung a pair of field glasses. His face was the face of a student, thin and ascetic, but his eyes had the cold gleam of the fanatic. They were deep and thoughtful, the eyes of a man who is used to looking at death.

He was eating a sandwich hungrily. He had eaten nothing since morning. He had been too excited to eat. He finished the sandwich, and, taking a flask from his pocket, he took a short draught. Then he returned the flask to his pocket. He paused for a moment, considering whether he should risk a smoke. It was dangerous. The flash might be seen in the darkness and there were enemies watching. He decided to take the risk.

Placing a cigarette between his lips, he struck a match. There was a flash and a bullet whizzed over his head. He dropped immediately. He had seen the flash. It came from the opposite side of the street.

He rolled over the roof to a chimney stack in the rear, and slowly drew himself up behind it, until his eyes were level with the top of the parapet. There was nothing to be seen — just the dim outline of the opposite housetop against the blue sky. His enemy was under cover.

Just then an armored car came across the bridge and advanced slowly up the street. It stopped on the opposite side of the street, fifty yards ahead. The sniper could hear the dull panting of the motor. His heart beat faster. It was an enemy car. He wanted to fire, but he knew it was useless. His bullets would never pierce the steel that covered the gray monster.

Then round the corner of a side street came an old woman, her head covered by a tattered shawl. She began to talk to the man in the turret of the car. She was pointing to the roof where the sniper lay. An informer.

The turret opened. A man's head and shoulders appeared, looking toward the sniper. The sniper raised his rifle and fired. The head fell heavily on the turret wall. The woman darted toward the side street. The sniper fired again. The woman whirled round and fell with a shriek into the gutter.

Suddenly from the opposite roof a shot rang out and the sniper dropped his rifle with a curse. The rifle clattered to the roof. The sniper thought the noise would wake the dead. He stopped to pick the rifle up. He couldn't lift it. His forearm was dead.

"Blast!" he muttered, "I'm hit."

Dropping flat onto the roof, he crawled back to the parapet. With his left hand he felt the injured right forearm. There was no pain — just a deadened sensation, as if the arm had been cut off.

Quickly he drew his knife from his pocket, opened it on the breastwork of the parapet, and ripped open the sleeve. There was a small hole where the bullet had entered. On the other side there was no hole. The bullet had lodged in the bone. It must have fractured it. He bent the arm below the wound. The arm bent back easily. He ground his teeth to overcome the pain.

Then, taking out a field dressing, he ripped open the packet with his knife. He broke the neck of the iodine bottle and let the bitter fluid drip into the wound. A paroxysm of pain swept through him. He placed the cotton wadding over the wound and wrapped the dressing over it. He tied the ends with his teeth.

Then he lay against the parapet, and, closing his eyes, he made an effort of will to overcome the pain.

In the street beneath all was still. The armored car

had retired speedily over the bridge, with the machine-gunner's head hanging lifelessly over the turret. The woman's corpse lay still in the gutter.

The sniper lay still for a long time nursing his wounded arm and planning escape. Morning must not find him wounded on the roof. The enemy on the opposite roof covered his escape. He must kill that enemy and he could not use his rifle. He had only a revolver to do it. Then he thought of a plan.

Taking off his cap, he placed it over the muzzle of his rifle. Then he pushed the rifle slowly over the parapet, until the cap was visible from the opposite side of the street. Almost immediately there was a report, and a bullet pierced the center of the cap. The sniper slanted the rifle forward. The cap slipped down into the street. Then, catching the rifle in the middle, the sniper dropped his left hand over the roof and let it hang, lifelessly. After a few moments he let the rifle drop to the street. Then he sank to the roof, dragging his hand with him.

Crawling quickly to the left, he peered up at the corner of the roof. His ruse had succeeded. The other sniper, seeing the cap and rifle fall, thought he had killed his man. He was now standing before a row of chimney pots, looking across, with his head clearly silhouetted against the western sky.

The Republican sniper smiled and lifted his revolver above the edge of the parapet. The distance was about fifty yards — a hard shot in the dim light, and his right arm was paining him like a thousand devils. He took a steady aim. His hand trembled with eagerness. Pressing his lips together, he took a deep breath through his nostrils and fired. He was almost deafened with the report and his aim shook with the recoil.

Then when the smoke cleared, he peered across and uttered a cry of joy. His enemy had been hit. He was reeling over the parapet in his death agony. He struggled to keep his feet, but he was slowly falling forward, as if in a dream. The rifle fell from his grasp, hit the parapet, fell over, bounded off the pole of a barber's shop beneath, and then clattered on the pavement.

Then the dying man on the roof crumpled up and fell forward. The body turned over and over in space and hit the ground with a dull thud. Then it lay still.

The sniper looked at his enemy falling, and he shuddered. The lust of battle died in him. He became bitten by remorse. The sweat stood out in beads on his forehead. Weakened by his wound and the long summer day of fasting and watching on the roof, he revolted from the sight of the shattered mass of his dead enemy. His teeth chattered, he began to gibber to himself, cursing the war, cursing himself, cursing everybody.

He looked at the smoking revolver in his hand, and with an oath he hurled it to the roof at his feet. The revolver went off with the concussion and the bullet whizzed past the sniper's head. He was frightened back to his senses by the shock. His nerves steadied. The cloud of fear scattered from his mind, and he laughed.

Taking the flask from his pocket, he emptied it at a draught. He felt reckless under the influence of the spirit. He decided to leave the roof now and look for his company commander, to report. Everywhere around was quiet. There was not much danger in going through the streets. He picked up his revolver and put it in his pocket. Then he crawled down through the skylight to the house underneath.

When the sniper reached the laneway on the street level, he felt a sudden curiosity as to the identity of the enemy sniper whom he had killed. He decided that he was a good shot, whoever he was. He wondered did he know him. Perhaps he had been in his own company before the split in the army. He decided to risk going over to have a look at him. He peered around the corner into O'Connell Street. In the upper part of the street there was heavy firing, but around here all was quiet.

The sniper darted across the street. A machine-gun tore up the ground around him with a hail of bullets, but he escaped. He threw himself face downward beside the corpse. The machine-gun stopped.

Then the sniper turned over the dead body and looked into his brother's face.

The Man He Killed

by Thomas Hardy

This poem is written as if it were being spoken by a country villager from the southwest of England. It contains a few words that may be unfamiliar to you. Before you read the poem, it may help you to know what they mean:

[1]*nipperkin: a small glass, holding a half pint or less.*
[2]*'list: enlist, join the army.*
[3]*traps: small possessions.*
[4]*half-a-crown: a small amount of money, roughly equal to an American quarter.*

"Had he and I but met
By some old ancient inn,
We should have sat us down to wet
Right many a nipperkin![1]

"But ranged as infantry,
And staring face to face,
I shot at him as he at me,
And killed him in his place.

"I shot him dead because —
Because he was my foe,
Just so: my foe of course he was;
That's clear enough; although

"He thought he'd 'list,[2] perhaps,
Off-hand like — just as I —
Was out of work — had sold his traps[3] —
No other reason why.

"Yes; quaint and curious war is!
You shoot a fellow down
You'd treat if met where any bar is,
Or help to half-a-crown.[4]"

Horatio Alger Is Dead

It is one hundred years ago. Sitting at the kitchen table, drinking tea after their evening meal, is the O'Hara family. They are not rich. They are not dirt poor. They are trying hard to make a living in this new country of theirs. Mr. O'Hara, a laborer, works 6 days a week, 10 hours each day. His oldest son, Liam, digs ditches for the city. The oldest girl, Eileen, has just come home from her first day as a sales clerk in the newly opened Willard's Department Store. She finishes her dinner, kisses her parents, grabs her books, and sets off for night school.

"Why doesn't Eileen stay home at night?" asks Kathleen, the youngest O'Hara.

"She wants to help make sure that you'll get the education you deserve. To do that, she'll need a better job," says Mrs. O'Hara.

"Hard work never hurt anyone," says Mr. O'Hara.

"I'm going to go to night school in the fall," adds Liam. "I want to get my high school diploma."

"Then what will you do?" This time young Kevin asks the question.

"Why then, I'll do what this chap does," Liam says, pointing to a magazine story. "I'll work hard, study hard, and make my way to fame and fortune — just like a real American."

The story Liam O'Hara was talking about was just one in a series of stories that inspired generations of Americans with their tales of how to be successful in America. Alger's young heroes worked hard from dawn to dusk, proved themselves, and were rewarded with a good office job and — sometimes this came first — the boss's daughter for a wife. These stories were the soap operas of their day. Like all soap operas, they told more than the plot of a story. They described what the society believed to be true about some important part of life. Alger didn't create the American myth that hard work by young people always leads to success. But he used it better than almost anyone.

Now that myth is being challenged by a new set of statistics compiled by Professor Ellen Greenberger of the University of California. The book she has co-authored, *When Teenagers Work: The Psychological and Social Cost of Adolescent Employment*, paints a bleak picture of the toll that part-time work takes on teenage school achievement, personal and social values, and future careers. Greenberger's research results are frightening. Here is some of what she has found out about the conflict between schoolwork and part-time work:

1. The students in the greatest danger of dropping out are students who work long hours in the early high school years.
2. Teachers whose classes are filled with students too tired to work and think respond by making few demands on their students.
3. Students who work take less difficult courses so that their work schedule is not jeopardized by the demands of the homework.
4. No study yet made shows that students who work make better grades.

What about learning the value of a dollar? That too, seems to be a myth that researchers are shattering. According to University of Michigan researcher Jerald Bachman, many students work, not because they have to, but because they want more spending money. And what do they spend the money on? Why, themselves. One teenager told researchers that he works 30 hours a week selling popcorn at an Atlanta theater. His motive is money. "I got this job so I could buy a VCR," he says. "Now that I've paid up, I'm going to get a movie camera." Linda McNeil, assistant professor of education at Rice University in Houson, explains it this way. "School is clearly not the center of their lives. The shopping mall is." Instead of learning the value of a dollar, teenagers are simply learning how to spend. If they are not encouraged to save — toward college or some other adult goal — they will start off on their own with expectations of spending all they earn on themselves. When they have to balance personal spending against the demands of rent, car payments, food, they won't be able to handle it.

Another danger for teenagers of having more money to spend is the temptation to spend it on the forbidden — drugs and alcohol. These can be a problem for any teen, including the ones who don't work, but as one researcher noted, "It's one thing to say that kids are going to do it; it's another thing to give them the money to do it." Furthermore, work itself can contribute to the increased use of drugs. Students who work long hours and then put in a full day at school are under a great deal of stress, which they may try to ease with drinking or other drugs.

What about the job itself? Isn't the right job a stepping stone to the future? Won't it provide the experience that will look good on a resume? Much as we would like to believe otherwise, the good part-time job that leads to a good future job is rare. Most of the teenagers working today are working at low-level jobs. Teenagers are grilling the burgers, serving them up, selling socks, and cleaning hotel and motel rooms. Furthermore, they're doing all this for minimum wage and, sometimes, for less than the minimum. If they are true part-timers, they don't get a benefits package. They are the last hired and the first fired.

Adding up all these facts produces, in the minds of many educators, a giant zero. They don't like what's happening to their students, and they want to do something about it. Right now. What they want to do about it is at the center of the latest controversy in education. One state is considering enacting a law that will limit the number of hours a high school student can work to no more than 12 hours during the week and 6 hours more on the weekend. Another educational system wants to restrict sophomores and juniors to 15 hours total a week and seniors to 20 hours.

Businesses that count on cheap and abundant teenage labor won't be too happy about changes like these. Teenagers themselves probably will feel outraged at any of these work restriction suggestions. The issue won't go away, however, because the truth behind the facts is also there to stay. Too many students are being graduated from high school without the old-fashioned abilities of reading, writing, and arithmetic. If they need to spend more time on the books and less on the job, society will have to put up with a few grumbles. In the long run, if we're lucky, the kids might even come back to thank us for saving them from a lifetime of flipping burgers because that was all they were able to do.

August Heat

by W.F. Harvey

August 20, 190–. I have had what I believe to be the most remarkable day in my life, and while the events are still fresh in my mind, I wish to put them down on paper as clearly as possible.

Let me say at the outset that my name is James Clarence Withencroft.

I am forty years old, in perfect health, never having known a day's illness.

By profession I am an artist, not a very successful one, but I earn enough money by my black-and-white work to satisfy my necessary wants.

My only near relative, a sister, died five years ago, so that I am independent.

I breakfasted this morning at nine, and after glancing through the morning paper I lighted my pipe and proceeded to let my mind wander in the hope that I might chance upon some subject for my pencil.

The room, though door and windows were open, was oppressively hot, and I had just made up my mind that the coolest and most comfortable place in the neighborhood would be the deep end of the public swimming bath, when the idea came.

I began to draw. So intent was I on my work that I left my lunch untouched, only stopping work when the clock of St. Jude's struck four.

The final result, for a hurried sketch, was, I felt sure, the best thing I had done.

It showed a criminal in the dock immediately after the judge had pronounced sentence. The man was fat — enormously fat. The flesh hung in rolls about his chin; it creased his huge, stumpy neck. He was clean-shaven (perhaps I should say a few days before he must have been clean-shaven) and almost bald. He stood in the dock, his short, stumpy fingers clasping the rail, looking straight in front of him. The feeling that his expression conveyed was not so much one of horror as of utter, absolute collapse.

There seemed nothing in the man strong enough to sustain that mountain of flesh.

I rolled up the sketch and, without quite knowing why, placed it in my pocket. Then, with the rare sense of happiness which the knowledge of a good thing well done gives, I left the house.

I believe that I set out with the idea of calling upon Trenton, for I remember walking along Lytton Street and turning to the right along Gilchrist Road at the bottom of the hill where the men were at work on the new tram lines.

From there onward I have only the vaguest recollections of where I went. The one thing of which I was fully conscious was the awful heat that came up from the dusty asphalt pavement as an almost palpable wave. I longed for the thunder promised by the great banks of copper-colored clouds that hung low over the western sky.

I must have walked five or six miles, when a small boy roused me from my reverie by asking the time.

It was twenty minutes to seven.

When he left me I began to take stock of my bearings. I found myself standing before a gate that led into a yard bordered by a strip of thirsty earth, where there were flowers, purple stock and scarlet geranium. Above the entrance was a board with the inscription —

CHAS. ATKINSON

MONUMENTAL MASON

WORKER IN ENGLISH

AND ITALIAN MARBLES

From the yard itself came a cheery whistle, the noise of hammer blows, and the cold sound of steel meeting stone.

A sudden impulse made me enter.

A man was sitting with his back toward me, busy at work on a slab of curiously veined marble. He turned round as he heard my steps and stopped short.

It was the man I had been drawing, whose portrait lay in my pocket.

He sat there, huge and elephantine, the sweat pouring from his scalp, which he wiped with a red silk handkerchief. But though the face was the same, the expression was absolutely different.

He greeted me smiling, as if we were old friends, and shook my hand.

I apologized for my intrusion.

"Everything is hot and glary outside," I said. "This seems an oasis in the wilderness."

"I don't know about the oasis," he replied, "but it certainly is hot, as hot as hell. Take a seat, sir!"

He pointed to the end of the gravestone on which he was at work, and I sat down.

"That's a beautiful piece of stone you've got hold of," I said.

He shook his head. "In a way it is," he answered. "The surface here is as fine as anything you could wish, but there's a big flaw at the back, though I don't expect you'd ever notice it. I could never make a really good job of a bit of marble like that. It would be all right in the summer like this; it wouldn't mind the blasted heat. But wait till the winter comes. There's nothing like frost to find out the weak points in stone.''

''Then what's it for?'' I asked.

The man burst out laughing.

''You'd hardly believe me if I was to tell you it's for an exhibition, but it's the truth. Artists have exhibitions: so do grocers and butchers; we have them too. All the latest little things in headstones, you know.''

He went on to talk of marbles, which sort best withstood wind and rain, and which were easiest to work; then of his garden and a new sort of carnation he had bought. At the end of every other minute he would drop his tools, wipe his shining head, and curse the heat.

I said little, for I felt uneasy. There was something unnatural, uncanny, in meeting this man.

I tried at first to persuade myself that I had seen him before, that his face, unknown to me, had found a place in some out-of-the-way corner of my memory, but I knew that I was practicing little more than a plausible piece of self-deception.

Mr. Atkinson finished his work, spat on the ground, and got up with a sigh of relief.

''There! what do you think of that?'' he said, with an air of evident pride.

The inscription, which I read for the first time, was this —

SACRED TO THE MEMORY

OF

JAMES CLARENCE WITHENCROFT

BORN JAN. 18TH, 1860.

HE PASSED AWAY, VERY SUDDENLY

ON AUGUST 20TH, 190–

''In the midst of life we are in death.''

For some time I sat in silence. Then a cold shudder ran down my spine. I asked him where he had seen the name.

''Oh, I didn't see it anywhere,'' replied Mr. Atkinson. ''I wanted some name, and I put down the first that came into my head. Why do you want to know?''

''It's a strange coincidence, but it happens to be mine.''

He gave a long, low whistle.

''And the dates?''

''I can only answer for one of them, and that's correct.''

''It's a rum go!'' he said.

But he knew less than I did. I told him of my morning's work. I took the sketch from my pocket and showed it to him. As he looked, the expression of his face altered until it became more and more like that of the man I had drawn.

''And it was only the day before yesterday,'' he said, ''that I told Maria there were no such things as ghosts!''

Neither of us had seen a ghost, but I knew what he meant.

''You probably heard my name,'' I said.

''And you must have seen me somewhere and have forgotten it! Were you at Clacton-on-Sea last July?''

I had never been to Clacton in my life. We were silent for some time. We were both looking at the same thing, the two dates on the gravestone, and one was right.

''Come inside and have some supper,'' said Mr. Atkinson.

His wife is a cheerful little woman, with the flaky red cheeks of the country-bred. Her husband introduced me as a friend of his who was an artist. The result was unfortunate, for after the sardines and watercress had been removed, she brought me out a Doré Bible, and I had to sit and express my admiration for nearly half an hour.

I went outside, and found Atkinson sitting on the gravestone smoking.

We resumed the conversation at the point we had left off.

''You must excuse my asking,'' I said, ''but do you know of anything you've done for which you could be put on trial?''

He shook his head.

''I'm not a bankrupt, the business is prosperous enough. Three years ago I gave turkeys to some of the guardians at Christmas, but that's all I can think of. And, they were small ones, too,'' he added as an afterthought.

He got up, fetched a can from the porch, and began to water the flowers. ''Twice a day regular in the hot weather,'' he said, ''and then the heat sometimes gets the better of the delicate ones. And ferns, good Lord! they could never stand it. Where do you live?''

I told him my address. It would take an hour's quick walk to get back home.

''It's like this,'' he said, ''We'll look at the matter straight. If you go back home tonight, you take your chance of accidents. A cart may run over you, and there's always banana skins and orange peel, to say nothing of fallen ladders.''

He spoke of the improbable with an intense seriousness that would have been laughable six hours before. But I did not laugh.

''The best thing we can do,'' he continued, ''is for you to stay here till twelve o'clock. We'll go upstairs and smoke; it may be cooler inside.''

To my surprise, I agreed.

We are sitting in a long, low room beneath the eaves. Atkinson has sent his wife to bed. He himself is busy sharpening some tools at a little oilstone, smoking one of my cigars the while.

The air seems charged with thunder. I am writing this at a shaky table before the open window. The leg is cracked, and Atkinson, who seems a handy man with his tools, is going to mend it as soon as he has finished putting an edge on his chisel.

It is after eleven now. I shall be gone in less than an hour.

But the heat is stifling.

It is enough to send a man mad.

No Place to Throw It

The Nielson family is in the car, on their way to Lake City, where they have rented a cottage for the month of August. Mrs. Nielson is driving. Mr. Nielson is giving directions. The three little Nielsons are in the back of the car. They are quiet now, munching and chewing happily on fast-food treats. Margie finishes her French fries first and crumples the paper bag they came in, just like her mother told her to. She looks around for someplace to throw the bag, just like her mother told her to. There's no trash bin in the car, so Margie leans over to the front of the car and says, "Here, Mom." Mrs. Nielson automatically takes her hand off the wheel and reaches back for the crumpled bag. She thinks: "What would they do with it if I wasn't here?"

As a nation, we have been a lot like Margie Nielson, producing trash and confidently handing it over to someone else to dispose of, expecting that the problem will be taken care of. But now it's time for us to grow up and take care of our own garbage because if we don't, we'll be up to our necks in trash before this century ends. Is this just another scare story to make us worry about something we never worried about before? Let's look at the facts.

First of all, what is in this stuff called trash or solid waste?

37% of it is paper and paperboard. (Margie's crumpled paper.)

18% of it is from lawns and yards. (The Nielsons mow their lawn a lot.)

10% of it is glass. (Baby Nielson eats a lot of baby food.)

10% of it is metal. (The Nielson family eats canned fruits and vegetables and drinks sodas.)

7% of it is plastics. (This includes the trash bags the Nielsons put their garbage in.)

18% of it is miscellaneous. (The old bed and chairs, the broken toys, discarded clothes make up part of this.)

Of course the Nielsons and families like them are still only part of the problem. Small businesses, big businesses, restaurants, department stores, newspaper stands, hospitals — all contribute their own kinds of mess to the growing pile. Just how big is the pile? One way to find out is to weigh it. Right now we produce about 133 million tons of fresh garbage a year, and trash experts predict that we will produce close to 300 million tons by the year 2000. Another way of sizing it up is to take a look at the largest landfill in the world.

New York City has the honor of possessing the world's largest and most crowded landfill (or dump). Fresh Kills landfill, on Staten Island, is unbelievably big — big enough to swallow 2,000 football fields. This pile of trash, which was opened about 40 years ago, will reach a height of 500 feet above sea level by the end of the century — making it the highest point on the Eastern Seaboard. At that time it will have to be closed, like so many other landfills.

Landfills have been used since the human race began. They have done a good job, but they can't handle the whole load. In the highly populated states of the Northeast, the trash load has become so enormous that most of the landfills have been used up. In New York State, for example, there were 1600 landfills in the 1960s; today there are only 300.

What about using the wide open spaces in the American West? Hauling trash by truck to any landfill costs money, and hauling it from Boston to Butte, Montana, just makes it costlier. Compacting the trash so that it is less bulky doesn't save much, because the compacted trash weighs more and haulage fees are based on weight. Also, Butte, Montana, may not want to deal with someone else's garbage, rejecting it with the classic NIMBY response: Not In My Back Yard. Trash experts expect this response. Landfills have to be managed and supervised or they will become dumping grounds for toxic wastes (not the kind of waste we're talking about here) that seep into the water system and pollute the land for miles around. Managing costs money — and the question remains, Who is going to pay? When that question is answered to everyone's satisfaction, states with more space than people might be willing to get income through trash.

A second way to get rid of trash is to burn it, but since the Clean Air Act of 1970, more and more incinerators have had to shut down because they can't meet the new standards. No one wants to go back to the dirty air we had almost 20 years ago with its related problems of increased lung disease and cancer, but what is a city like Philadelphia to do? All but two of its incinerators have been closed because they couldn't pass inspection. In addition to being a source of air pollution, they were inefficient at the burning job they were supposed to do. Tons of ash and unburnables were left behind that had to be hauled off to the nearest landfill. Next year, the nearest available landfill will be in the Central American country of Panama.

Incinerators can be improved. Some European countries that have been incinerating their trash for more than

30 years have developed a technology for burning waste cleanly and efficiently. Before we follow their lead, our citizens would have to learn to separate their garbage into burnables and nonburnables; incinerator operators would have to control the results of burning plastics. Right now, when certain plastics burn, the gases that are produced form compounds called "dioxins," a deadly poison. Any city or state that elected to build more incinerators would hear a huge roar of NIMBY from each community.

Recycling was supposed to be the cure-all for mounting trash problems. It certainly sounded good. People would separate their trash, the town would collect it and turn it over to engineers who would transform the trash — by burning — into energy or electricity. The burning, of course, became a problem, except in the most modern incinerators, but the worst problem of all was the people problem. People who live in small suburban areas with garbage cans in their back yards may grumble at first but they soon get accustomed to the routine of separating trash. But people who live in big city apartment houses have no place to separate or store the separated trash. What is needed to make recycling work is dollar pressure. If trash producers had to pay a fine for each load of trash that wasn't separated, habits would change overnight.

There is another way of handling trash that may be the simplest — and the most difficult — way of all. Make less trash. The next time you go to the dime store or the supermarket, take a close look at the amount and the size of "packaging" that surrounds each item you buy. What if you, the consumer, had to pay a garbage tax for each over-packaged item you bought? Would you still buy it? Manufacturers would howl if they were told they couldn't put their small bottle of hand lotion in the big box, but if they had to pay a big-box tax, they, too, might change their minds.

The Nielsons are home from vacation. As they unpack their bags, they fill wastebasket after wastebasket with summer's leftovers. A single flip-flop sandal, some smelly shells, at least two cups of sand, torn magazines, broken toys, crumpled papers, useless ballpoint pens, used up tubes of sun block, and four pairs of sunglasses with cracked lenses. Mr. Nielson turns to his older son and say: "OK, Tom, it's your turn to take out the garbage."

"Where will I put it?" asks Tom.

Mr. Nielson's face has that exasperated look on it that parents get when their kids ask pointless questions. He starts to speak, when Mrs. Nielson says, "He's right, you know. Where will we put it?"

Warming Up the World

Is the world becoming a warmer place to live? Many scientists think so, but they also think that warmer isn't necessarily better. The greenhouse effect, a gradual increase in temperature worldwide caused by an accumulation of gases in the atmosphere, may have disastrous results.

There seems to be little doubt that the Earth is getting warmer. In fact, it has been doing so since the middle of the 18th century, when the Industrial Revolution began the chain of environmental changes that has led to the problems in today's atmosphere. By the year 2030, the Earth's temperature is expected to be 3 to 8 degrees Fahrenheit warmer than it is now. A temperature increase of this size has never happened before in such a short time.

What is responsible for this dramatic change? The culprit seems to be a group of gases known as the "greenhouse gases." The greenhouse gases are harmful for two reasons. First of all, because they trap heat, these gases are responsible for a gradual but significant warming of the environment. The effects of this change in temperature are not yet completely known, but they will certainly include changes in where crops are grown and what is grown; flooding of coastal areas; and an increase in the number and severity of tropical storms. Second, some of the greenhouse gases also damage the ozone layer — the layer of a special kind of oxygen that screens out the harmful rays of the sun known as ultraviolet light.

The expected environmental changes are complex. If we continue to produce greenhouse gases at the same rate we do now, the next 50 years will bring destruction of 5 to 9 percent of the ozone layer. With this loss of protection against the sun's ultraviolet rays, at least 15,000 more people each year will become victims of melanoma, a deadly form of skin cancer caused by exposure to ultraviolet light. The increase in global temperature will cause glaciers to melt, raising the level of the oceans enough to destroy vast areas of coastline. Cities like New Orleans and Miami will disappear.

The temperature of the oceans will grow warmer too, causing an increase in tropical storms. It is now estimated that if the average annual temperature is only 2 degrees warmer than it is now, the number of hurricanes will double. It will get hotter everywhere. For example, instead of having one day a year in which the temperature goes above 100 degrees, Washington, D.C., will have twelve days of blistering heat. Instead of 36 days with temperatures above 90 degrees, there will be 87 days. Some areas of the world will benefit from the warmer temperatures, but many more will be devastated. Because the increased heat will also affect rainfall, the grain-growing area of the United States will grow dry and hot, unable to produce the crops we depend on. Other areas will get more rain than they can use.

Both plant and animal life that has adapted to the climate of particular parts of the world will suddenly be faced with dramatic changes in temperature, rainfall, and levels of carbon dioxide. Even ocean life will be affected. The warmer water and increase in ultraviolet light will make it impossible for some species of aquatic life to survive, while others increase disproportionately. For example, the plankton — tiny sea plants and animals, that supply food for many of the fish we eat — are sensitive to ultraviolet light and will fail to reproduce. Blue-green algae, on the other hand, are resistant to ultraviolet light and will increase in number, leaving even less room for the threatened plankton.

The primary culprit among the greenhouse gases is carbon dioxide, the gas we release when we exhale. Unfortunately, we are not the only ones emitting carbon dioxide. It is also released when fossil fuels such as coal and oil are burned. As our dependence on these fuels has grown over the past century with the increasing industrialization of the world, so has the amount of carbon dioxide in the air. The carbon dioxide traps heat from the sun along the Earth's surface, just the way the glass of a greenhouse does.

Obviously, we could start cutting back on the amount of carbon dioxide in the air by reducing our dependence on fossil fuels, or at least by controlling the pollutants they produce. Some controls — for example, of automobile emissions — are required now in the United States. But others — for example, of the carbon dioxide that is a by-product of heavy industry — are more difficult to establish and enforce. Even economic pressures don't always work. Stiff fines could be imposed for ignoring pollution-control measures, or taxes could be increased for industries that, by their very nature, pollute the environment with carbon dioxide and other destructive gases. So far, however, we have not been very successful in passing the bills that would impose such fines and taxes.

Suppose we were to consider a second alternative — outlawing fossil fuels. What would we use instead? We would need efficient, inexpensive alternatives not only to gasoline for automobiles and heating oil for houses but also to the fuels that keep many of our major industries going. Even if we could find such alternatives and require their use in this country, what would we do about the many developing countries that are racing to catch up with the industrialized world? Because such measures might slow their progress, they would be even more unwilling than we are to adopt safeguards and substitutes. In fact, you need only to breathe the air outside the United States to discover that even now, very few other countries control fuel emissions as extensively as we do.

Another factor has contributed to the concentration of carbon dioxide in the Earth's atmosphere. There has been a decrease in the amount of forest land that would ordinarily absorb carbon dioxide. Normally, large tracts of forest are sufficient to control the level of carbon dioxide in the atmosphere. Plants take carbon dioxide from the air to use in photosynthesis, and they return oxygen to the air. But as areas such as the Brazilian rain forest are leveled so that the land can be farmed or developed in other ways, the Earth loses its natural ability to keep carbon dioxide in check. As we have seen with carbon dioxides, fines for those who destroy forest land or monetary rewards for those who develop alternative routes to economic growth might provide a partial solution, but establishing and enforcing such regulations has proved, so far, a major obstacle.

And how do we, in the United States, halt the clearing of forests in countries that are struggling to raise their standard of living? To protect the Earth's atmosphere, we must cooperate with other countries in setting limits on such practices as changing forests into grazing land.

Finally, there are the other "greenhouse gases." Prime among these are the chlorofluorocarbons (CFC's). Until recently CFC's were used as propellants in aerosol spray cans. Although that use has been outlawed in the United States since 1978, CFC's are still used here and in many parts of the world in refrigerants, industrial solvents, and plastic foams — as well as in aerosol sprays in countries other than the U.S. In addition, a 20 to 50 percent increase in the amount of methane in the atmosphere is expected within the next 50 years, as a result, probably, of increased rice production and an increase in the number of grazing animals grown on farms (many where those rain forests have been cut down). Both rice paddies and animals such as cows produce methane as a by-product.

Again, one of the reasons that it is difficult to arrive at a solution is that the greenhouse effect is a global problem. Making aerosol spray cans illegal in the United States does nothing to control the use of CFC's in other parts of the world, or their use in this country for other purposes. As soon as aerosol can production was halted here, the use of CFC's in other products — for example, the plastic foam boxes in which eggs and fast food hamburgers are packaged — increased. There are some alternatives — CFC's that are less harmful, fluorocarbons without chlorine so that they don't affect the ozone layer, ways of recycling CFC's rather than releasing them into the atmosphere — but each one is either more expensive or less efficient (and therefore more costly in the long run) than existing CFC's.

What can we do to prevent the massive and dangerous changes scientists now predict? Unfortunately, it may already be too late to do anything about some of the changes. It takes a long time for the greenhouse gases to make their way to the stratosphere, where they go to work on the ozone layer. The gases whose effects we will feel 50 years from now have already been released into the atmosphere.

DATE DUE

APR 2 2 2005			
GAYLORD			PRINTED IN U.S.A.